GOLD
experience
2ND EDITION

WORKBOOK

A2+
**Pre-Preliminary
for Schools**

CONTENTS

Listening	Speaking	Writing	Review
topic: hanging out with friends **task:** multiple choice (pictures)	**topic:** family time **task:** describing a photo	**topic:** what makes a place great **task:** article	unit check 1
topic: joining a club **task:** notes completion	**topic:** free time activities **task:** collaborative task	**topic:** hobbies and personality **task:** online profile	unit check 2
topic: storytelling **task:** multiple choice	**topic:** something funny happened to me **task:** telling a story	**topic:** short stories **task:** story	unit check 3 review: units 1–3 (p30)
topic: schools: past, present and future **task:** multiple choice	**topic:** relaxing with friends **task:** long turn	**topic:** school exchanges **task:** email	unit check 4
topic: fashion **task:** sentence completion	**topic:** shopping **task:** describing a photo	**topic:** app and website reviews **task:** review	unit check 5
topic: day trips **task:** multiple choice (pictures)	**topic:** a hiking trip **task:** collaborative task; follow-up questions	**topic:** the natural world **task:** article	unit check 6 review: units 1–6 (p56)
topic: food and eating **task:** multiple choice	**topic:** preparing food; ordering food **task:** describing a photo	**topic:** a food festival **task:** email	unit check 7
topic: a school skiing trip that went wrong **task:** multiple choice	**topic:** a present to take home **task:** collaborative task	**topic:** a holiday story **task:** story	unit check 8
topic: a sci-fi convention **task:** sentence completion	**topic:** language for guessing **task:** long turn	**topic:** an invitation **task:** email	unit check 9 review: units 1–9 (p82)

READ ON

1 Name the objects in the picture.

1 g _ _ _ _ _
2 f _ _ _ _ _ _ _
3 g _ _ _ _ c _ _ _ _ _ _ _ _ _
4 c _ _
5 p _ _ _ _
6 h _ _ _ _ _
7 p _ _ _ _ _ c _ _ _
8 s _ _ _ _ _ _ _ _ _
9 T- _ _ _ _ _
10 b _ _ _ b _ _ _ _

2 Read the web posts. Which objects from Ex 1 are mentioned?

Birthday Board

TODAY'S

Everyone with a birthday today – post on our birthday board! Tell us what presents you received, big or small, and if you're having a great day!

Jazz

It's my fourteenth birthday today and yes, it's a great day! There's a party tonight, and I've had some fantastic presents. My parents got me a bodyboard – because I love going in the water when we're on holiday. It's a really expensive one and it's got a picture of a white horse on it – it's so cool! I love it. My gran's present was a guitar book. I'm learning to play the guitar and this book has got some great music to practise. My younger brother hasn't got a lot of money so he put his favourite pencil case in a bag for me. He's so lovely. It's a plastic fish with a big mouth and that's where you put the pens and pencils! Inside it there was a photo of him and me too! I also got a new skateboard from my best friend. What a day!

Mike

Thirteen today and some fantastic presents. I cycle a lot and bikes and clothes are expensive. Mum and dad bought me a new helmet. I can wear it in my race next Saturday. Perhaps it will help me win another cup! My older sister gave me a new cover for my phone. But it's red. She loves red but I don't! I'm going to try to change it. My younger sister got me a cool T-shirt with the name of my favourite band on it. It's a bit big but I really like it. My favourite, favourite present was from my uncle and aunt. I broke my games controller last month and now I've got a new one! I can't live without my games controller!
This evening we're going to the cinema to see the new superhero film. Very good day!

3 Read the posts again and decide if the statements are true (T) or false (F).

1 Jazz's parents bought her a picture of a white horse. ....
2 Jazz got something to help her play a musical instrument. ....
3 Mike's favourite present is from his younger sister. ....
4 Jazz received a skateboard from someone she doesn't know very well. ....
5 Mike is younger than Jazz. ....
6 One of Mike's presents is the wrong size. ....

4 Complete the sentences with the correct words.

1 **This / Those** skateboard is old now and I need a new one.
2 My best friends are Will and Stuart. **He / They** often help me with homework.
3 Mum **can / can't** ride a bike but she's a good car driver! Strange!
4 Who do **those / that** football boots belong to? **My / Me** boots are at home.
5 My gran always gives **my / me** tea and cakes when I visit **she / her**.
6 The children are in the garden. Tell **they / them** that it's dinner time.
7 **Our / Ours** dog always wakes us up really early, but we don't mind!
8 If the weather is bad, you **should / shall** wear a coat.

5 🔊 S.1 Listen to Kenny, Seth and Jimmy talking about holidays in Spain. Match the speakers to the photos.

A ....

B ....
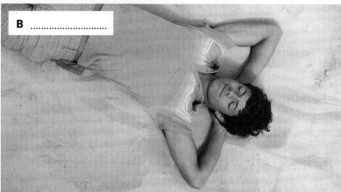

C ....

6 🔊 S.2 Listen again. Are the sentences true (T) or false (F)? Correct the false sentences.

1 Kenny can't swim. ....
2 Seth's parents can speak Spanish well. ....
3 Seth can talk to people in Spain. ....
4 Jimmy sits in the sun for a long time. ....
5 Jimmy makes new friends in Spain. ....

Corrections: ....
....

7 Choose the correct words to complete the message.

> Evie – Sunburn again! ¹**Are** / **Be** careful. ²**Doesn't** / **Don't** forget to put on sun cream and ³**you sit** / **sit** in the sun for a short time only. ⁴**Not** / **Don't** lie there at lunchtime – it's too hot. ⁵**You wear** / **Wear** a sun hat to protect your head and ⁶**to remember** / **remember** your sunglasses. ⁷**Drinks** / **Drink** lots of water! That's it. ⁸**Have** / **has** a lovely holiday 😊. Oh, and ⁹**wear** / **wearing** beach shoes because the sand is hot.
> Love Tina – sorry, I sound like your mum!

8 Match the questions (1–6) with their answers (A–F).

1 What's your name? ....
2 Where do you live? ....
3 How old are you? ....
4 Who do you live with? ....
5 How do you usually travel to school? ....
6 What are you looking forward to this year? ....

A In Margate, near the town centre.
B Our holiday in New York, in September.
C My parents and two sisters.
D 15 next birthday.
E My dad drives me.
F It's Diana.

9 Imagine it's your birthday today. You are going to write a post for the Birthday Board in Ex 2. Complete the useful phrases with the correct words.

about   because   favourite   for   really   without

1 I got a book from my brother. It's .... a man who likes animals.
2 My aunt bought a T-shirt .... me.
3 My .... present is a new phone.
4 I can't live .... my phone.
5 I love this picture .... it has great colours.
6 I was .... surprised to get this coat from my grandma.

10 Plan your post.

1 Say what presents you received and who from.
2 Explain why you like / don't like them.
3 Choose your favourite present and say why.

11 Write your post in about 100 words.

1 There's no place like home

READING

1 Look at the photo and read part of Ella's blog about her travelling life. Complete it with the correct words.

community   freezes   hang out   lift   open   pressure

Our travels

HOME **NEW POSTS**

This is my second year of travelling with my family now. When my parents first talked about selling our home and going travelling, I was very ¹............................ with them and said I wasn't sure about it. At fifteen years old you just want to go to school and ²............................ with your friends, right? But in fact it's great. We're now part of a different ³............................ of families who choose to travel around, and I'm definitely pleased that I don't have the ⁴............................ of school exams anymore! We meet lots of different people – today we gave two students from Sweden a ⁵............................ , and they were really fun to chat to. Tomorrow we're going into the mountains. It's really cold there, and we want to see what a river looks like when it ⁶............................ – it sounds cool to me!

2 Read Ella's blog in Ex 1 again. Decide if the sentences are true (T) or false (F).

1 Ella spoke to her parents honestly when they suggested going travelling. ....
2 Ella thinks that teenagers enjoy doing organised activities with their friends. ....
3 Ella thinks that families who travel around help each other and feel connected to each other. ....
4 Ella used to get worried when she had exams. ....
5 Today, two students from Sweden travelled with Ella and her family. ....
6 Ella wants to see a river in very hot weather. ....

3 Read an interview with Ella on page 7. Match the headings with the correct paragraph.

1 What about your education? ....
2 What are the best and worst things about travelling all the time? ....
3 Was it hard to leave your friends behind? ....
4 What's it like being with your parents all the time? ....

4 Read the interview again. Decide if the sentences are true (T) or false (F).

1 Ella and her family drive to a new place every day. ....
2 Ella doesn't enjoy having to keep her room tidy. ....
3 Ella often argues with her parents now. ....
4 Ella has a better relationship with her brother now. ....
5 It isn't easy for Ella to contact her friends back home. ....
6 Ella feels disappointed that she can't relax with her friends now. ....
7 Ella and her mum both find maths difficult. ....
8 Ella and her family sometimes visit places to help with Ella's studies. ....

5 What do you think Ella would say about her life now?

A I love it, but my brother finds it really difficult.
B There are some difficulties, of course, but there are lots of good things, too.
C I thought it was a good idea at first, but now I'm not so sure.
D We have lots of problems as a family that we didn't have before.

6 Match the words in bold in the interview with the meanings.

1 sad because you are on your own and not with other people
....
2 normal ....
3 untidy ....
4 not nice or enjoyable ....
5 a good thing ....
6 to feel sad because you can't do something that you did before
....

6

When home  is the **open road**

Ella doesn't live in a house or flat. Her home is on the road, travelling around America with her parents and her brother, Scott. Her parents decided to sell their home and buy a big RV (mobile home), because they wanted to see different parts of the country and experience a different way of life. Her dad has his own internet business, so he works from an office in the RV. We asked Ella what life is like when your home is always on the move.

 A .... ?

My favourite thing is that every day is different! We don't always travel somewhere new, but I never know when I wake up what's going to happen. Life is never boring! The other great thing is meeting people. When you live in a house or flat, you spend a lot of time inside. We're always outside, so we meet some really interesting people. The most difficult thing is that I can't be **messy**. I've got my own room in the RV, but it's really small, so I can't leave things lying around – that's annoying!

 B .... ?

A lot of people ask me if I have all the **usual** arguments with my parents – about staying up late, doing jobs around the home, that kind of thing. But when you live together in such a small space it just isn't possible to argue – it's too **horrible** for everyone! In fact, things are much better now. Because we spend a lot of time together, I talk to my parents and my brother, Scott, a lot more. We're more like friends than family now.

 C .... ?

That was the biggest problem for me at the start. Saying goodbye was definitely difficult. But we're online and I have my phone of course, so it isn't difficult to keep in contact with them and stay up to date with what's going on in their lives. And I'm never **lonely**. Every time we go to a new place I make new friends. So I've got a lot more friends now than I had before. But I guess I do **miss** just hanging out with people, watching a movie or chatting.

 D .... ?

My mum is my teacher now, but I help her plan what I'm going to study each month. I do a lot of studying online. I also have an online teacher for maths. That's my worst subject, and Mum isn't brilliant at it either! It isn't easy to study on your own, but the **advantage** is that I can choose what to learn about. I love learning about animals, so we try to get to places where I can see wild animals – that's really useful. I think I want to study biology at college when I'm older.

---

7 Complete the sentences with words from Ex 6.

1 The big .... of travelling is that you see lots of new places.

2 My sister is really .... – she leaves her things all over the house!

3 My best friend moved to a new city and I really .... seeing her every day.

4 I sometimes feel .... if I'm on my own in the flat.

5 My brother likes doing all the .... things that teenagers do, like riding his skateboard.

6 I can't eat this soup – it's ....!

GRAMMAR

a/an, the and no article

1 Choose the correct words to complete the sentences.

1 I think that **families / the families** are really important.

2 My sister wants to be **a / an** actor.

3 I'm learning to play **a / the** piano.

4 There isn't much for **the young people / young people** to do in my town.

5 I have **dinner / the dinner** with my family most evenings.

6 My mum can speak **Spanish / the Spanish**.

7 My uncle lives in **USA / the USA**.

8 Some parents put **pressure / the pressure** on their children to do well at school.

9 Was **a / the** film good last night?

10 There isn't **a / an** university in my town.

2 🔊 1.1 **Complete what the people say about their families with *a/an, the* or no article (–). Then listen and check.**

(A) I'm ¹........................... only child but it isn't ²........................... problem for me. I like spending ³........................... time with my parents, and I've got ⁴........................... friends I can see if I want to be with people my own age.

(B) I come from ⁵........................... big family with nine children, and ⁶........................... house where we live is always very busy, especially in ⁷........................... mornings, when everyone is trying to get ready for ⁸........................... school!

(C) I've got ⁹........................... younger brother and he's really annoying! Like, he always wants to play ¹⁰........................... same computer game that I want to play, at ¹¹........................... only time I'm free to play! There are often ¹²........................... arguments in our house! But other days we get on really well.

3 Read the sentences about Sam and her interesting family. Which sentences use articles correctly? Write C for correct or I for incorrect.

1 Sam Briggs lives in a small town in USA. ....

2 She lives with her parents and 24 brothers and sisters. ....

3 Sam's brothers and sisters come from all over the world. ....

4 Two of her brothers are from Mexico, and three sisters are from the Africa. ....

5 All the children had problems in their own countries, so Sam's parents offered them a home. ....

6 They have big house, with 10 bedrooms. ....

7 Sam works hard at school, and she wants to study art when she's older. ....

8 Sam loves her brothers and sisters and is really happy that she has unusual family! ....

4 Read Helen's blog about her life on a small Scottish island. Complete it with *a/an, the* or no article (–).

My home is on ¹........................... small Scottish island. It's called Lewis and it's two and a half hours by boat from ²........................... west coast of the mainland. About two thousand people live on ³........................... island, and I know most of them! A lot of ⁴........................... tourists visit in the summer, too. People often ask me what it's like to live here, so I'll tell you. Yes, we *do* have ⁵........................... electricity and ⁶........................... cars! In fact, we have most of ⁷........................... things that you can get in ⁸........................... towns and cities, even ⁹........................... coffee shops and ¹⁰........................... cinema. But it's different here because life is very relaxed. Of course, we have ¹¹........................... stress sometimes, but not very much. I get on well with my family, and I know everyone else my age, so I can always ask ¹²........................... friend for ¹³........................... help if I need it. And it's easy for me to find out what's happening in other parts of ¹⁴........................... world, because of course we have ¹⁵........................... internet!

5 Read some questions people have left Helen on her blog. Complete them with *a/an, the* or no article (–).

1 Is there .... school on the island, or do you have to go across .... sea to the mainland?

2 I love meeting .... new people. Do you ever get fed up with seeing .... same people every day?

3 Do you want to find .... job on the island when you leave school, or do you want to move to .... big city like Edinburgh?

4 I think I would enjoy .... life on Lewis. Can I come and visit you for .... holiday?

VOCABULARY

around town

1 Complete the crossword.

Across

1 You wait here if you want to catch a bus. (two words)

5 You might sit here if you're tired while you're shopping in town.

6 This is where you put things that you don't want. (two words)

Down

2 This is where people walk next to a road.

3 This is a place where you can leave your bicycle. (two words)

4 You can use this place to go to the other side of the road.

2 Complete the sentences with the correct words. Use one word from each box.

apartment	art	department	skate	sports	swimming

block	centre	gallery	park	pool	store

1 There are some amazing paintings at the new ....

2 We play our football games at the ....

3 It's hot – let's go to the .... – the water's always nice and cool there!

4 Jake's new flat is in that .... over there.

5 I never buy clothes in the .... – it's too expensive.

6 A lot of people hang out with bikes and skateboards at the ....

3 🔊 1.2 Complete the fun facts with the correct words from Exs 1 and 2. Listen and check your answers.

city fun facts

1 The biggest .... in the world is at a hotel in Alfonso de Mar in Chile. It's over 1 km long – that's a lot of water!

2 There are nearly 20,000 .... in London. Most of them have a roof to keep you dry, but at the others you may get wet while you're waiting to travel.

3 In the UK, it's against the law to throw waste from your home into a .... in the street! The ones on the street are only for things you need to throw away while you're out.

4 There were .... in the streets over 2,000 years ago. In very old Roman cities you can still see places where people could get across the road safely.

5 The tallest .... in the world is in New York. It's at 432 Park Avenue, and it has flats on 85 floors.

Extend

4 Match the words (1–7) with their meanings (A–G).

1 clinic   **4** palace   **7** tourist information centre

2 college   **5** police station

3 factory   **6** stadium

A a place where things are made using machines ....

B a place where police officers work ....

C a place where people can go to watch sport ....

D a place where you can see a doctor ....

E a place where visitors can get information about the area ....

F a large house where a king or queen lives ....

G a place where people can study ....

5 Read what the people are saying. Where are they, or where are they going? Use the places 1–7 from Ex 4.

1 'Hurry up! The game starts in half an hour!' ....

2 'What time does the museum open, please?' ....

3 'I'm so stressed – I've got exams all this week!' ....

4 'I'm arresting you – you need to come with me!' ....

5 'They produce 5,000 cars a week here.' ....

6 'If your leg is still painful tomorrow, come back here.' ....

7 'Look – there's the princess! She's waving from the window!' ....

1 There's no place like home

LISTENING

1 Look at the five sets of pictures and read the questions. Match each word below with the picture it matches.

bowling .5A. camping .... diving .... snacks ....
film .... game .... hiking .... ice skating .... museum ....
music .... sailing .... water-skiing .... shopping ....
skate park .... theme park ....

1 Where do the boys agree to go on Saturday? ....

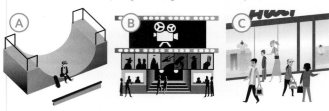

2 What new sport does the girl want to do? ....

3 Which trip won the youth club members' vote? ....

4 What should the boy bring on Friday? ....

5 Which activity does Anna like doing with her family? ....

2 e 🔊 1.3 Listen and choose the correct answer, A, B or C in Ex 1.

3 🔊 1.4 Complete sentences 1–5 from the audio with the correct words from the box. Listen and check.

| brilliant choice fit perhaps suggested |

1 I've got a .... new trick I want to show you.
2 You have to be very .... and strong for that.
3 The most popular .... was the camping trip.
4 He wants to have some snacks, so .... you could get some.
5 Mum .... maybe a trip to a museum.

4 Match the words from Ex 3 (1–5) with their meanings (A–E).

A maybe ....
B the thing that someone chose ....
C with a strong, healthy body ....
D said something as an idea ....
E very good ....

some, any, (how) much, (how) many, all, a little, a few, a lot of

5 Choose the correct words to complete the sentences.

1 I'd like to invite **some** / **any** / **a little** friends round tonight.
2 How **much** / **many** / **a lot of** people were at the party?
3 I'm sorry, we don't have **much** / **any** / **some** snacks.
4 Some fun activities don't cost **many** / **much** / **some** money.
5 It's easy to organise a party if you have **a little** / **a few** / **much** help from your parents.
6 Dan has got **a little** / **any** / **a lot of** computer games!
7 Can you bring **a little** / **a few** / **much** drinks with you?
8 **All** / **Every** / **A few** my friends love this new film!

6 Read the magazine article about the perfect teenage hangout and think of one word which best fits each gap.

A place of my own

Ben Radcliffe has the perfect hangout space – a wooden hut in his garden! Ben's hut is warm and comfortable inside. There's a carpet on the floor, and there are a ¹........................... chairs, but there aren't very ²........................... places to sit. 'If I have a lot ³........................... friends here, we have to sit on the floor,' Ben says. There's electricity and heating in the hut, and Ben can also use the wifi from inside the house. 'It's great. I use my hangout hut every day,' Ben says. 'I keep ⁴........................... my computer games here, and I can listen to music or watch films. And what if he's noisy? 'It's impossible to be completely quiet, but I don't make ⁵........................... noise,' he says. 'The only problem is that there aren't ⁶........................... windows, so it isn't possible to see outside. But of course that also means that no one can see in!'

SPEAKING

1 Look at the photo. Complete the sentences describing it with the correct present tense form of the verbs in brackets.

1 The photo .... (show) four people.
2 I can .... (see) two teenagers and their parents.
3 They .... (not talk) to each other.
4 The family .... (sit) in the kitchen.
5 I think they .... (have) breakfast.
6 The boy .... (wear) some headphones.
7 The dad .... (work) on his laptop.
8 The boy and his mum .... (look at) their mobile phones.

2 Choose the correct words in the sentences about the photo in Ex 1.

1 The dad is on the **left** / **right**.
2 The boy is **next to** / **behind** his mum.
3 I think they are **in** / **on** their home.
4 There is a microwave **between** / **behind** them.
5 There is some toast and butter **in** / **on** the table.
6 There is a glass of juice **behind** / **in front of** the girl.

3 Look at the photo below. Match the kinds of information for describing photos (1–6) with the sentences (A–F).

1 the people ....
2 the place ....
3 the weather ....
4 the clothes ....
5 the activities ....
6 the people's feelings ....

A I think it's summer, but it isn't very hot.
B The photo shows two teenagers.
C They both look happy and are smiling a little.
D I can see some water behind them, so I think they're near a lake.
E They are cooking some food over a fire.
F They are wearing trainers.

4 **e** Use the ideas in Ex 3 and practise describing the photo. Try to add more information. Record yourself.

5 🔊 1.5 Listen and compare your ideas with the answer on track 1.5.

WRITING

an article

1 Choose the correct words to complete the sentences that describe a place someone visits.

1 It's .... the south of Spain.

   A at   **B** near of   **C** in

2 It's .... a region called Andalucia.

   A in   **B** at   **C** on

3 It's .... the coast.

   A in   **B** in front of   **C** on

4 The house is right .... the sea.

   A behind   **B** by   **C** into

5 It's also .... the mountains.

   A near   **B** on   **C** from

2 Choose the best connector in each sentence.

1 The weather is warm **and** / **but** it's also sunny most of the time.

2 There's a train station there **so** / **but** you can get to the town easily.

3 I love this place **so** / **because** it's so beautiful.

4 There are no shops, **so** / **but** I don't mind that.

5 There's a big swimming pool **because** / **so** you can swim every day.

6 I can invite lots of friends **so** / **because** the living room is quite big.

3 Read the task. Then read a student's article. Does it answer all the questions in the task?

A place that I visit

Think about a place that you visit.

Where is it?

Who do you go there with?

What is special about it?

Write an article answering these questions. We will publish all the articles on the school website.

4 Look at the bold prepositions in the student's article. Then choose the correct prepositions to complete the sentences (1–6).

1 We sometimes have lunch **in** / **to** a little café.

2 Our apartment is **in** / **on** the second floor.

3 There's a restaurant at the top **from** / **of** the building.

4 We sometimes go **to** / **in** the cinema to see a film.

5 I love walking **about** / **around** London.

6 My aunt lives **at** / **in** Paris.

5 Plan your ideas for an article about a place that you visit.

Where it is	
Who I go with	
What is special about it	

6 **e** Use your notes and write an article on a place that you visit. Write about 100 words.

My uncle's apartment

I sometimes visit my uncle's apartment **in** New York. It's **on** the top floor **of** a typical Manhattan apartment block. It's quite big, so I can go there with my family and a few friends.

The apartment is clean and modern, and it has great views **of** a park. The best thing about it is that when I stay there I can enjoy everything about the city. I can go **to** shows on Broadway, walk **around** the shops and eat **in** typical New York restaurants.

I love going **to** my uncle's place!

UNIT CHECK

1 Complete the sentences with the correct words.

bike rack   bus stop   crossing   pavement   rubbish bin   seat

1 The cinema is on the other side of the road, so we need to find a ....
2 Shall we sit on this .... and have a rest for a few minutes?
3 I'll wait for you on the .... outside the department store, then we can go in together.
4 Don't drop that paper on the ground – put it in the .... !
5 Hurry up, we need to get to the .... before 10.30!
6 Lots of people cycle to college, so there's a big .... there.

2 Read the clues and complete the words.

Where are we?

① You can play tennis and football here.
s_o__s c_ _ _ _e

② People take their skateboards here.
s_ _ _e p_ _k

③ You can see famous paintings here.
a_ _ g_ _ _ _ _y

④ A lot of people live in one of these.
a_ _ t m_ _t b_ _ _k

⑤ You can buy lots of different things here.
d_ _ _ t m_ _t s_ _ _e

⑥ Families play in the water here.
s_ _ m_ _g p_ _l

3 Complete the sentences with the correct words.

clinic   college   factory   information centre
palace   police station   stadium

1 I've got an appointment to see the doctor at the .... next week.
2 Two officers arrested the thief and took him to the ....
3 They make engines for aircraft in this ....
4 The king and queen live in a beautiful .... in the old city.
5 I want to go to .... and study business.
6 More than 20,000 fans watch their team play every week at this ....
7 They have lots of information about sightseeing and local events at the tourist ....

4 Complete the sentences with *a/an, the* or no article (–).

1 I need to get .... new phone.
2 There's a big department store in .... city centre.
3 It might rain, so take .... umbrella with you.
4 My sister doesn't eat .... meat.
5 It's often hot and sunny in the south of .... Italy.
6 Are you .... student?
7 My uncle travels all over .... world.
8 I don't like .... bananas.
9 Can you speak .... French?
10 My aunt has bought .... new house. She really likes .... house, but she doesn't like her neighbours!
11 A lot of .... people come to .... UK to work.
12 Let's meet at .... swimming pool in .... hour.

5 Choose the correct words in the dialogues.

A: How [1]**many / much** people do you want to invite?
B: Only a [2]**few / little**.

A: There are [3]**some / any** great shops in this town!
B: Yes, but there aren't [4]**some / any** that are cheap enough for me!

A: [5]**All / Every** the parks in the city are very popular.
B: I know. I walk through the park [6]**a lot of / every** day when it's sunny.

A: How [7]**many / much** money have you got?
B: Only [8]**a little / some**. Not enough for a pizza!

6 Read the blog post about home. Choose the best words to complete it. There are two words you don't need.

all   any   every   few   how   lot   much   some

It's only when you go away that you find out [1]...........................
much home means to you. I spent six weeks in South America last summer. It was a great experience, but there were a [2]........................... of things that I missed about home. The first thing was friends! Of course, I made a [3]........................... new friends, but new friends just aren't the same as old ones! Then there was my family. At home, my sister seems to do at least one thing to annoy me [4]........................... day, but when I was hundreds of miles away I was amazed how fond of her I felt! There are [5]........................... things that always feel strange when you're away from home – like sleeping in a different bed and eating different food. And of course you can't be in a bad mood – you have to be polite and cheerful [6]........................... the time, which isn't easy!

READING

1 Complete the sentences with the words in the box.

link   press   program   search for   share   site

1 I love travelling and I always take lots of photos and post them online. It's great to .... them with all my friends.

2 My new tablet is brilliant, but I need a special .... for drawing cartoons, which is my main interest.

3 There's an excellent .... where you can learn how to do unusual hobbies – it's really useful.

4 The CD player in Dad's car isn't working. I .... 'open' but it stays closed.

5 To get information for the project, ... 'computer game competitions' and there are lots of websites.

6 I'm sending you a .... to the travel website that my mum always uses.

2 e Read the introduction on a forum about hobbies. Choose the correct answer.

1 The website is for

  A people who have no hobbies.

  B people who have too many hobbies.

  C people who want to teach and learn about hobbies.

  D people who don't like their hobby.

2 When someone writes about their hobby, they should

  A give lots of information about their hobby.

  B arrange to take people to their club meetings.

  C give online lessons about their hobby.

  D write about a hobby they think other people might like.

Hobby ↻ Swap

New members | **Profile** | 🔍

Are you looking for an interest that's different? Have you got an unusual interest that you think others would like too? Post an introduction about your favourite hobby on our Hobby Swap page and you can teach and learn different activities. You can chat online to people and then meet up at our Hobby Swap weekend in May. Some of the things that people love and do are amazing! Could YOU teach someone about your hobby? Which would YOU like to try?

 Emma Like Share

Hi! I'm sure some people think my interest is a bit unusual. It's cricket! You can see cricket matches on TV and in many English towns and villages at the weekends. It's a very traditional English sport played in a large field. Everyone wears white clothes and one person throws a ball which another person has to hit a long way. Some people think it's a crazy game because it's quite slow and people stand around a lot. But it isn't! It's great fun! There are lots of cricket clubs and it doesn't matter if you're young or old – everyone can enjoy it. I'm thirteen and I love it!

I'm looking for an activity to do indoors when the weather's too bad for playing cricket. Any suggestions?

 Hugo Like Share

People say that my interest is a bit strange. It's called Toy Voyaging. The idea is that you send a toy around the world and get photos of it in different places. There's a special site where you can register to be a host and look after someone's toy. People send the toys by post and say what their toy wants to do while it's there. The hosts put photos on the site and people follow their travels and adventures! Does this sound crazy? Perhaps it is a bit! But it's great fun. You find out about lots of places in the world and chat to different people too.

I want to find another unusual interest – nothing too sporty, perhaps something I can do with other people?

Katya Like Share

You may not believe this, but my interest is stand-up comedy! That means I tell jokes to an audience and hope that they laugh! When I was young my friends often wanted me to tell them funny stories. Now I go to under-18s comedy clubs where people stand up on stage and do it! It's scary at first but it's an amazing feeling to hear people laughing.

I'd like another interest – probably a sport because I need to get fit. But it's got to be interesting and a bit unusual!

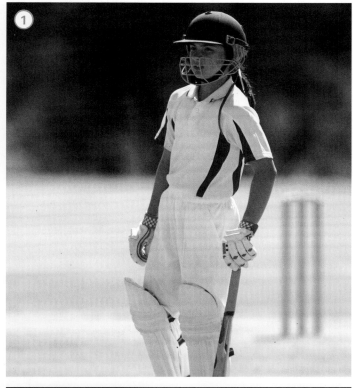

3 Read the forum posts and match the pictures (1–3) with the people Emma (E), Hugo (H) and Katya (K).

1 .... **2** .... **3** ....

4 Read the forum again. Match each sentence (1–6) with a poster (E, H or K).

1 You can learn about different countries with this person's interest. ....

2 This person's activity can be frightening for beginners. ....

3 You need a computer for this person's interest. ....

4 This person says the activity is more interesting than other people think. ....

5 This person's interest makes people laugh. ....

6 This person wears special clothes for this activity. ....

5 Match the words (1–6) with their meanings (A–F).

1 look for ....

2 swap (something for something) ....

3 sharp ....

4 match ....

5 register ....

6 find out (about) ....

7 audience ....

8 get fit ....

A learn

B like a knife, something like this cuts

C give information about yourself, e.g. to join a club

D try to find

E group of people watching or listening to something

F become strong, usually from doing exercise

G exchange / give something and receive something different

H a competition usually between two sports people or a team

6 Complete the sentences with the correct word(s) from the forum posts.

audience   find out   fit   look for   race   register   sharp   swap

1 Let's .... stories about our holidays. Tell me about yours first.

2 .... on the website and you can get lots of useful information.

3 The acting in the show was very good and the .... loved it.

4 This knife isn't very .... – I can't cut anything!

5 I'd like to .... when the art club starts.

6 I need to go running to get .... before the competition. I don't do enough exercise.

7 The .... is for under-18s and the winner gets a cup.

8 I need to .... my tennis shirt – it's not in my bag.

GRAMMAR

present simple and present continuous

1 🔊 **2.1** Listen to James talking about swimming. How is his swimming today different from his usual swimming?

....

....

2 🔊 **2.2** Complete the sentences from the interview with the correct form of the verbs in brackets. Listen again and check.

1 I .... (ask) people about their favourite sports.
2 I usually .... (train) five times a week.
3 I .... (wait) for the bus to go swimming at the moment.
4 My training .... (start) at 5.30.
5 I often .... (win) my races.
6 At the moment we .... (have) a break from training.

3 Put the words in the correct order to make sentences.

1 after / play / sometimes / football / school / I

....

2 is / on / brother / always / Saturdays / busy / my

....

3 plays / my / ever / games / computer / hardly / friend

....

4 read / don't / magazines / often / I

....

5 mum / to / does / drive / your / usually / work?

....

6 go / on / rarely / Sundays / shopping / we

....

7 am / tired / often / swimming / I / after

....

8 dinner / always / my / cook / doesn't / dad

....

4 Choose the correct words to complete the sentences.

1 They **rebuild / are rebuilding** the sports centre in Matcham's Road.
2 I **think / am thinking** that starting a new sport is a good idea.
3 The school **looks / is looking** for a new sports teacher.
4 Where **do you play / are you playing** football on Fridays?
5 My friend **doesn't often play / isn't often playing** tennis.
6 When **does the match usually finish / is the match usually finishing**?
7 We **do / are doing** a project on famous sports people in class.
8 I **need / am needing** to practise my tennis – it's terrible!

5 Complete the blog with the correct present tense form of the verbs given.

go   look   love   not do   play (x2) · start   try

Most people in my family ¹........................... football – sometimes watching, sometimes playing. My dad ²........................... for a local team every weekend with his friends. They usually lose! At the moment Dad ³........................... to get fitter because he gets tired quickly! But he ⁴........................... very well. He still can't run for a long time.

We are all fans of our city team – Leicester F.C. Luckily, they ⁵........................... very well at the moment. When they play at home we usually ⁶........................... to the stadium to watch them. But when they play away in another city we watch them on television. Their next match is against Manchester United on Saturday. It ⁷........................... at 3.00. We ⁸........................... forward to it. Good luck, Leicester!

6 🔊 **2.3** Complete the conversation with the correct present form of the verbs in brackets. Listen and check.

A: Why ¹........................... (you / sit) here? You ²........................... (look) really tired. Are you OK?

B: I ³........................... (have) a break! It's my tennis club's big competition today. We ⁴........................... (have) them every year in June. There are lots of matches. I ⁵........................... (do) very well today. I'm in the final later. It ⁶........................... (not start) until 3.30. So, I ⁷........................... (rest) now!

A: I see! I ⁸........................... (not play) tennis. It's too tiring! Good luck later.

VOCABULARY

practising and improving

1 Complete the blog with the correct words.

brilliant   competitions   improving   practises   skills   successful

My sister, Adele, is only nine years old but she's quite famous in our town! She's a **¹**............................ dancer and can do lots of different dances! She **²**............................ with her partner after school and they often take part in **³**............................ . They often win so she's got lots of prizes in her room. She loves learning new **⁴**............................ and her dancing is **⁵**............................ every week. My parents think she can have a career in dancing and be very **⁶**............................ .

2 Choose the correct words to complete the sentences.

1 Wow! Look at those test results! You're **doing / making** excellent progress!

2 Don't **use / waste** time chatting online. You've got homework!

3 I'm **taking / making** part in a tennis competition tomorrow.

4 I **go / spend** about two hours practising the piano every evening.

5 Is your training **going / getting** well? Mine isn't!

6 Good! You're **doing / making** very well. Keep running!

7 You need to practise the song again and again to **go / get** it right.

3 Which sentences in Ex 2 do you think these people would say?

A A friend ....

B A parent ....

C A teacher or trainer ....

4 🔊 2.4 Match the sentences from Ex 2 (1–7) with the responses (A–G) below. Listen to check.

A I know. But I need to talk to Sophie.

B OK, but when can I stop?

C Thanks! My parents are really pleased.

D OK, thanks. The competition's on Saturday.

E I know – I'm making lots of mistakes.

F Good luck! Can I come and watch?

G That's a long time! I only do half an hour!

5 Choose the correct answers.

Practice
makes perfect?

Some people say you need to start young and spend a lot of **¹**........ practising if you want to get **²**........ at a sport. It's true that you have to do things again and again to get them right. But you need motivation and ambition to really **³**........ . When children are really interested in a sport they are happy to train hard to get good **⁴**........ . They enjoy **⁵**........ part in competitions and winning. But, many successful child sports stars lose interest when they're in their teens. They get tired of practising and there are other important things for them to do. They don't want to **⁶**........ hours swimming up and down a pool while their friends are going to the cinema or gigs!

	A	**B**	**C**	**D**
1	minutes	time	moments	work
2	well	fine	better	correct
3	pass	gain	succeed	reach
4	results	notes	achievements	points
5	playing	taking	making	doing
6	lose	last	use	waste

Extend

6 Match the words (1–5) with their meanings (A–E).

1 score ....

2 contest ....

3 champion ....

4 prize ....

5 compete ....

A a person who wins a lot of competitions

B the results of a sports competition, e.g. a football match

C to take part in a competition

D the person who wins a competition can get this

E another word for competition

7 Complete the sentences with the correct words from Ex 6.

1 Our team won the match! The .... was 5–0!

2 Jack and Brad often .... in table tennis competitions. Jack's our school ....

3 The winner's .... is a gold cup. It's very heavy!

4 The .... continued for two hours.

LISTENING

1 🔊 **2.5** You will hear a girl called Kelly talking to a group of people about a club she goes to. Listen and decide who she is talking to.

A her classmates

B other club members

2 Read the task and look at the gaps. What kind of information do you need? Choose the correct option on the right.

1 The music club meets every	day / place
2 The group for younger children starts at	place / time
3 Kelly goes to .... for her club meeting.	person / place
4 The music club members sometimes work with a famous	object / person
5 Kelly prefers learning how to use the	object / date
6 The first performance of the show is on	date / time

3 🅔 🔊 **2.6** Listen again. For each question in Ex 2, write the correct answer in the gap above. Write one or two words, or a number, or a date or a time.

subject and object questions

4 Do the questions ask about the subject of the verb? Answer yes (Y) or no (N).

1 Who teaches at your dance club? ....

2 What do you learn in your extra classes? ....

3 How many students go to the dance club? ....

4 Who do you go to the club with? ....

5 Who organises the trips to dance competitions? ....

6 What happens after the classes? ....

5 Match these responses with a question from Ex 4 (1–6).

A I usually go with Louisa. ....

B There are about 30 of us. ....

C A lady called Josie runs the classes. ....

D Josie organises those too. ....

E We do moves to faster music – it's hard! ....

F Sometimes we hang out but often we're all really tired so we go home. ....

6 Decide if the underlined words are the subject (S) or object (O) of the sentences. Then write questions to ask about the underlined words.

Example: <u>Tim</u> likes rock music. ..S..
Who likes rock music?
....

1 <u>Jamie Banks</u> sometimes talks to the group. ....
....

2 Danny Parker writes <u>horror stories</u>. ....
....

3 The club meets <u>on Wednesdays</u>. ....
....

4 <u>The meeting place</u> changes every week. ....
....
....

5 <u>The children's group</u> is doing a play tonight. ....
....

6 They sing <u>pop songs</u> in music club. ....
....

7 Read an advertisement for a show. Choose the correct words to complete the text.

A world of stars

Saturdays, 8 p.m.

Channel 16

And another TV talent show starts this Saturday. I can hear the questions already. Who **¹wants / does want** another talent show? Why **²we need / do we need** to listen to more bad singers? Who **³decides / does decide** the TV programmes for Saturday nights? Well, this show is different! The singers are all under fifteen years old and they are from fifteen different countries. There's a pop singer from Japan, a rock singer from Norway, etc. Which singer **⁴wins / does win** the contest? Where **⁵the winner comes / does the winner come** from? What sort of music **⁶the winner sings / does the winner sing**? Wait and see – it's a very interesting show.

SPEAKING

1 Look at the pictures in the exam task at the bottom of the page. Match the activities (1–6) with the pictures (A–F).

1 doing card tricks ....
2 taking photos of wildlife ....
3 playing football ....
4 playing a board game ....
5 going for a walk ....
6 cooking dinner on a campfire ....

2 Read the exam task and the comments (1–6) about what students should do. Decide if the comments are true (T) or false (F).

> You are going camping with your family and some friends. Here are some activities you could do there. Talk together about the different activities you could do when you're camping, and say which would be the best.

1 One student talks about the pictures and then the other student talks about them. ....
2 The students need to suggest some new activities for a family to do on a camping trip. ....
3 The students discuss the activities together and then make a decision. ....
4 The students choose their favourite activity. ....
5 The students ask for their partner's opinion and give their own. ....
6 The students choose one activity to talk about. ....

3 Reorder the words to make useful questions and phrases for discussing the pictures.

1 playing / think / football / do / about / you / what / ?
2 good / would / a / football / be / idea / ?
3 about / football / what / playing / ?
4 you / what / think / do / ?
5 a / idea / that's / great
6 it's / my / idea / opinion / good / in / a

4 e 🔊 2.7 Listen to a student talking about three of the pictures. When you hear a beep, reply to her by following the instructions (1–5). Record your answer.

1 agree or disagree
2 give two or three reasons
3 suggest another activity
4 give your opinion
5 ask for your partner's opinion

5 Listen to your recording. Did you follow all the instructions (1–5) in Ex 4? Did you use any of the phrases from Ex 3?

Activities on a camping trip

WRITING

a profile

1 Read the sentences. Which adjectives describe the people?

careful   clever   confident   friendly   honest   polite   quiet   serious

1 My sister never drops or breaks things. ....

2 Our dog doesn't make a lot of noise. ....

3 Jade can stand up on stage and talk to people with no problem. ....

4 My young brother always says please and thank you. ....

5 Helena always speaks to new members of the club, so they don't feel alone. ....

6 My friend can do lots of complicated things on his computer. ....

7 I try to always tell the truth and not lie to people. ....

8 Our science teacher doesn't laugh, even when we make funny jokes. ....

2 Choose the correct words to complete the sentences.

1 I like / **I'd like** to join another club next term.

2 I like / **I'd like** doing card tricks for my family.

3 My friend **likes** / **would like** to become a teacher.

4 Katy and Peter **like** / **would like** going to the dance club.

5 We **like** / **'d like** doing homework together.

6 My mum **likes** / **would like** to learn Italian cooking.

3 Complete the sentences about you and your best friend.

1 I like ....

2 I'd like ....

3 My friend likes ....

4 My friend would like ....

4 Read the online profile about Jessie's best friend, Eva. Complete the middle column in the table below with the correct information.

5 Now complete the right-hand column in the table with information about one of your friends or someone in your family.

6 **e** Use your notes from Ex 5 and write an online profile of the person you chose and his / her hobbies. Write about 100 words.

Extend

7 Match the adjectives (1–8) with the meanings (A–H).

Someone who …

A is calm and not worried

B is always telling other people what to do

C always does what he / she says they are going to do

D is happy and smiling

E is happy to give things to others

F isn't clever / intelligent

G isn't afraid in dangerous situations

H is unhappy or angry because someone has something that they want

1 bossy

2 jealous

3 reliable

4 relaxed

5 stupid

6 generous

7 brave

8 cheerful

my best friend

By Jessie G

My best friend's name is Eva and she's fifteen years old, like me. She's very funny and likes telling jokes. I can't be serious when we're together! Eva likes art and drama. She goes to art club on Tuesdays and to drama club on Thursdays. She's very confident and she's a great actor. She's also very clever — she's good with software and she likes making animation films. She spends every evening working on her films. She's making a film about a group of dogs and cats at the moment. It's very funny. In the future Eva would like to write stories for films. What a great idea! I'd like to have a famous friend.

Name:	1 Eva	1
Age:	2	2
Words to describe him / her:	3	3
Clubs he / she goes to:	4	4
When:	5	5
Something he / she is doing at the moment:	6	6
Something he / she would like to do in the future:	7	7

UNIT CHECK

1 Complete the sentences with the correct words.

better   make   part   right   spends   waste   well   work

1 I often take .... in swimming competitions and I sometimes win.

2 My school grades need to get ....

3 I sometimes .... a lot of time trying to choose what to wear in the morning!

4 I'm writing a short story at the moment and it's going ....

5 My dad usually does card tricks at parties but they don't always ....

6 I often .... mistakes when I'm speaking English.

7 My friend never .... time checking his homework.

8 We have to practise the dance again and again to get it ....

2 Find the words in the wordsnake and match them with the meanings.

placchesszteamorcontesterprizecanimationinngymnasticsychampionbagaming

1 Playing on a computer: ....

2 A sort of film: ....

3 A board game: ....

4 The person who wins a competition: ....

5 A type of competition: ....

6 You win this in a competition: ....

7 A group of people in a match: ....

8 A sport: ....

3 Choose the correct answers.

1 My friend is very .... and she often helps me at school.

   A relaxed   **B** clever   **C** crazy

2 My older brother is .... and gets angry if I don't do what he says.

   A bossy   **B** brave   **C** careful

3 Katy is .... because I've got a new phone and she hasn't.

   A honest   **B** serious   **C** jealous

4 It's .... to say 'thank you' – not just take something and walk away!

   A honest   **B** polite   **C** confident

5 Jack is a .... student and sometimes the teacher forgets he's there!

   A cheerful   **B** quiet   **C** careful

4 Put the adverbs in the correct places in the sentences.

1 My dad doesn't go running at the weekend. (often)

2 It is hot in Madrid in the summer. (always)

3 I see my aunt and uncle during the week. (rarely)

4 We are at home on Saturdays. (hardly ever)

5 Our swimming teacher brings her daughter to the swimming pool. (occasionally)

6 We don't watch films in class. (usually)

5 Complete the sentences with the correct present form of the verbs.

1 The sports centre .... at 8.30 tomorrow morning. (open)

2 I .... Italian at the moment because I .... speaking to people when we're on holiday. (study / like)

3 I .... a lot of great apps on my new phone. (have)

4 My dad usually .... in town but he .... from home for a few days. (work / work)

5 I .... a lot about making animation films. (not know)

6 My brother .... to drive and he .... very well. (learn / do)

6 Write questions about the words in bold.

1

A .... ?

   Mr Green teaches **English**.

B .... ?

   Mr Green teaches English.

2

A .... ?

   Our next tennis lesson is **on Thursday**.

B .... ?

   Our next tennis lesson is on Thursday.

3

A .... ?

   Olly is meeting **Caroline** after school.

B .... ?

   Olly is meeting Caroline after school.

4

A .... ?

   My mum doesn't like cheese sandwiches.

B .... ?

   My mum doesn't like **cheese sandwiches**.

5

A .... ?

   Sandy and Anna are watching **a horror film** at the moment.

B .... ?

   Sandy and Anna are watching a horror film at the moment.

3 Read all about it

READING

1 Read the news story. Complete it with the correct words.

flowing   picked   remote   stuck   stuff   tie

Last Saturday afternoon, friends Matt White and Adam Bailey decided to take their small boat out onto the river near their village. However, the boys didn't know that the river was very full that morning, and the water was ¹........................... fast. They couldn't control the boat and it raced away down the river. Luckily, after a while it got ²........................... at an island and they managed to get hold of a tree and pull themselves out. However, they didn't manage to ³........................... their boat up, and it soon disappeared. They were safe on the island, but they were also worried they might have to spend the night there. No one lived there and it felt very ⁴........................... . Soon, however, a man saw them waving and called the rescue services. The police soon came and ⁵........................... them up, and they arrived home safely. Although they lost their boat and all their ⁶........................... that was on it, Matt and Adam feel very lucky.

2 Match the words from Ex 1 with their meanings.

flow   pick up   remote   stuck   stuff   tie

1 to fix something to a place with string or rope ....
2 a long way away from towns and cities ....
3 unable to move ....
4 to move forwards in a steady way ....
5 to collect someone from a place ....
6 things ....

3 Read the news story about a rescue at sea. Choose the sentence that best describes the story.

A A man managed to stay alive for 54 days at sea, and says he'll never go on a boat again.
B A man is angry that it took rescuers 54 days to find him after he became ill at sea.
C A man caught fish and drank rainwater to stay alive after his boat was damaged at sea.

4 **e** Read the story again. Five sentences have been removed from the text. Choose the correct sentence (A–H) to fill each gap. There are three extra sentences which you do not need to use.

A Everything went well for the first few days.
B Then, quite by chance, he found a solution.
C He was very glad to see the rescue helicopter.
D He was still in pain from the injury to his hand.
E On 24 July he packed food and other things onto his boat.
F The storm continued for several days.
G James was worried the boat might sink.
H The first thing he thought about was fresh water.

5 Read the story again. Decide if the sentences are true (T) or false (F).

1 James hates being on his own at sea. ....
2 James couldn't use the radio to call for help after the storm. ....
3 James thought people would come and rescue him after only a few days. ....
4 There was nothing to eat on the boat. ....
5 James discovered by accident that he could catch fish. ....
6 James wants to continue sailing. ....

6 Match the words in bold in the story with their meanings.

1 tools and machines that you use to do something ....
2 stay alive ....
3 fix something that is damaged ....
4 very bad weather, with strong winds and rain ....
5 you use this for catching small fish ....
6 spoke to ....

7 Complete the sentences with the correct form of words from Ex 6.

1 If you feel ill, you should .... a doctor.
2 In freezing weather, people and animals have to keep warm to ....
3 My phone is broken – do you know anyone who can .... it for me?
4 The big .... last night damaged some buildings in the town.
5 You must have the right safety .... to go climbing.
6 Fishing boats often use large .... to catch thousands of fish.

54 DAYS AT SEA

A man was rescued from his boat yesterday after spending 54 days lost at sea. Twenty-two-year-old James Gladstone has always spent a lot of time sailing and is comfortable being alone at sea. **¹........** .
He then set off for a ten-day trip, not expecting any problems.

²........ However, just as he was thinking about returning home, James suddenly found himself in the middle of a **storm**. When a sudden strong wind hit the boat, James fell and hurt his hand badly. The wind also broke parts of the boat and damaged its electrical **equipment**, so James had no radio and no way of controlling the boat.

Because he was injured, James couldn't **repair** the boat, so he knew he just had to wait for someone to come and rescue him. **³........** . He knew he only had a small amount left, and it might be several weeks before he was rescued. He therefore used buckets and pots to collect rain, and tried to drink only a small amount each day.

James had only brought enough food for ten days, and he knew he would soon run out. Of course, the sea around him was full of fish, but he couldn't think how to catch them, as he didn't have a **net**. **⁴........** He was washing his clothes in the sea at the back of the boat when he noticed a fish stuck in his shirt. So, using this, he managed to catch enough food to **survive**.

When rescuers arrived at the boat, they were amazed at how well James was. **⁵........** . But apart from that, he was healthy and cheerful. His parents had **contacted** the emergency services when he didn't return home as expected, and a rescue helicopter went to find him. James admits his adventure was scary at times, but he definitely won't stop sailing!

3 Read all about it

GRAMMAR

past simple and past continuous

1 Choose the correct verb forms to complete the sentences.

1 I **found** / **was finding** some money while I **walked** / **was walking** through the park.

2 Jack **got** / **was getting** home and **saw** / **was seeing** that there was a letter for him.

3 While we **swam** / **were swimming** in the sea, someone **stole** / **was stealing** our clothes!

4 Everyone in the crowd **started** / **was starting** singing when he **scored** / **was scoring** his third goal!

5 I **fell** / **was falling** when I **ran** / **was running** for the bus.

6 Lisa **told** / **was telling** her mum all about it when she **arrived** / **was arriving** home.

7 My brother **became** / **was becoming** ill while we **camped** / **were camping** last year.

8 We **decided** / **were deciding** to play tennis because the sun **shone** / **was shining**.

2 🔊 3.1 Complete the news stories with the correct verb forms. Listen and check.

CRAZY NEWS!

Girl catches tennis ball in drink

At three o'clock last Saturday afternoon, 15-year-old Amy Jones ¹........................... (watch) a game of tennis at Wimbledon when something funny happened. One of the players suddenly ²........................... (hit) the ball badly, and it ³........................... (fly) straight towards Amy. At that moment, Amy ⁴........................... (drink) a cup of orange juice. Without thinking, she ⁵........................... (hold) up her cup of orange juice and ⁶........................... (catch) the ball in it! Everyone in the crowd ⁷........................... (think) it was very funny!

Man survives bear attack and shark bite in same year

Glen Turner must be the luckiest (or unluckiest) man alive. Six months ago a bear ⁸........................... (attack) him while he ⁹........................... (walk) in the mountains in Colorado, USA. Glen ¹⁰........................... (fight) the bear, which finally ¹¹........................... (run) off, leaving him with just a few cuts. Then yesterday, Glen ¹²........................... (swim) in the sea off Florida. He ¹³........................... (not see) that a shark – one of the most dangerous animals in the sea – ¹⁴........................... (follow) him. The shark ¹⁵........................... (bite) Glen's leg, but he ¹⁶........................... (manage) to swim safely back to the beach. He's fine now and hoping for a quiet few months!

3 Rewrite each pair of sentences as one sentence. Use the word in brackets.

1 I arrived home. It was raining.
It .... home. (when)

2 Paul was playing football. He hurt his leg.
Paul .... football. (while)

3 Sara left school. She got a job.
Sara .... school. (when)

4 I met George in New York. I was living there.
I .... in New York. (while)

5 I told Ana the joke. She laughed.
Ana .... the joke. (her)

6 We were at the bus stop. We saw Greg.
We .... at the bus stop. (waiting)

4 Complete the news story with one word in each gap.

● ● ● ◁ ▷   🔍 🏠

A young woman from Manchester thought of a clever idea to keep her identity secret. She couldn't believe her luck ¹........................... she received a letter saying she had won a large amount of money in a competition. But she ²........................... want many people to know about her win because she thought strangers might contact her to ask for money. So what ³........................... she decide to do? She thought about it for a few days, then she ⁴........................... an idea. On the day for giving out the prizes, the organisers of the competition were very surprised to see that the woman ⁵........................... wearing a huge smiling emoji to hide her face. She continued to wear the emoji even while the organisers ⁶........................... making their speeches and giving her the money. So even now, no one knows who won all that money!

24

VOCABULARY

adjectives

1 Complete the crossword.

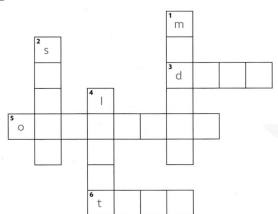

Across
- **3** boring
- **5** not special in any way
- **6** very small

Down
- **1** not old
- **2** making you feel afraid
- **4** not heavy

2 Complete the adjectives to match their meanings.

1 very old

a _ _ _ _ _ t

2 different or very good in some way

s _ _ c _ _ l

3 when something is good because you can do things with it

u _ _ f _ l

4 not light or bright

d _ _ k

5 interesting and fun

e _ _ _ t _ _ g

6 made of an expensive yellow metal

g _ _ d

7 very big

h _ _ e

8 worth a lot of money

v _ l _ _ b _ _

9 made of wood

w _ _ _ _ n

---

3 🔊 3.2 Amy, Greg and Sasha like looking for things on their local beach. Complete what they say about it. There are two adjectives you don't need. Then listen and check.

| ancient | exciting | huge | light | ordinary | scary | useful | valuable |

It's always ¹............................ when you find something strange on a beach. I was walking on a beach a few years ago when I found a ²............................ number of bananas – there were thousands of them! I think they'd fallen off a ship.

I once found twenty toy ducks on a beach near me. They were just ³............................ yellow plastic ducks, but it was really funny to see them there. It seems they came from a ship that sank, and of course because they're very ⁴............................ they just floated on top of the water and ended up on the beach.

I keep hoping I'll find something ⁵............................ on the beach near me, but in fact I don't think I'll ever find anything to make me rich. I did once find a wooden box that's quite ⁶............................ for keeping things in.

4 Write the words in the correct order to make more things that Amy, Greg and Sasha have found on beaches.

1 a .... (valuable / ring / old)

2 some .... (chairs / ordinary / wooden)

3 some .... (gold / coins / ancient)

4 a .... (huge / hand / plastic / blue)

5 some .... (modern / tools / useful)

6 a .... (bottle / beautiful / glass)

Extend

5 Choose the correct words to complete the meanings of the adjectives in bold.

1 Something that is **brand new** is **not very new / completely new**.

2 A **basic** idea is **simple / difficult** to understand.

3 Something that is **excellent** is very **bad / good**.

4 Something that is **noisy is / isn't** quiet.

5 A **cute** animal or child looks **nice / scary**.

6 Something that is **funny** makes you **laugh / cry**.

7 Something that is **pretty is / isn't** nice to look at.

8 Something that is **unusual is / isn't** ordinary.

6 Choose the correct adjectives to complete the sentences.

1 Carl told us some very **funny / pretty** jokes – we couldn't stop laughing!

2 You have to learn the **excellent / basic** dance moves first, before you try the more difficult ones.

3 That car looks quite **unusual / noisy** – I've never seen one like that before!

4 You work really hard, so I'm sure you'll get **cute / excellent** exam results.

5 Those flowers are really **pretty / noisy**!

LISTENING

1 🔊 3.3 You will listen to an interview with a woman called Naomi who teaches people how to be good storytellers. What things do you think Naomi will mention? Listen and check.

A why people love listening to stories

B why some people are good at storytelling

C choosing a good story to tell

D using notes while you tell your story

E using your voice to make your story more interesting

F how to stand or sit while you tell a story

G how to end your story well

2 e 🔊 3.4 Listen again and choose the correct answers.

1 Naomi first became interested in storytelling

   A when she was at school.

   B when she was at a festival.

   C when she was travelling.

2 What is the main thing that makes someone a great storyteller?

   A their natural ability

   B plenty of practice

   C good training

3 According to Naomi, you should always choose a story that

   A you really like.

   B has a good ending.

   C is suitable for your audience.

4 When preparing to tell a story, Naomi says you should

   A take out parts that your audience might find boring.

   B change some details to make the story more modern.

   C make a personal connection to the story.

5 What is the most important thing to do while you are telling a story?

   A Use a range of different voices.

   B Make eye contact with your listeners.

   C Move your arms and hands a lot.

6 At the end of a story, Naomi says you should

   A make it clear to people what the story means.

   B encourage your listeners to guess the ending.

   C allow people to understand the story in their own way.

3 🔊 3.5 Complete sentences 1–5 from the audio with the correct adjectives from the box. Listen and check.

complicated confused dull original wonderful

1 I heard this .... storyteller!

2 Is the ending exciting or .... enough?

3 Should I take out the .... parts, or make it more modern?

4 It's not .... You don't need to be an actor, and you certainly don't need to move your arms around madly.

5 You don't want to leave your audience feeling .... and guessing how the story ends.

4 Match the words from Ex 3 with their meanings.

1 with new and different ideas ....

2 very good ....

3 difficult to do or understand ....

4 boring ....

5 feeling that you don't understand something ....

someone, anyone, nothing, everything, etc.

5 Choose the correct words to complete the advert for a storytelling course.

Storytelling
made easy

[1]**Everyone / Everything** enjoys a good story, so why not train to be a storyteller? [2]**No one / Anyone** is a completely natural storyteller – we all have to learn. We've got great trainers here who can teach you [3]**everything / someone** you need to know about the art and skill of storytelling. There isn't [4]**nothing / anything** difficult on the course and we will give you full support. If you're interested, call the number below and [5]**someone / anyone** will explain all the details of the course to you. So apply today – there's [6]**nothing / something** to stop you becoming a great storyteller!

SPEAKING

1 Complete the sentences you can use when you are telling a story. There are two words or phrases you don't need.

about   after   funny   happened   tell   think back   true story

1   This is a story .... my brother.

2   I'm going to .... you about something funny that I saw last week.

3   This is a true story that .... to me when I was playing football once.

4   When I .... to what happened, I can't believe how lucky I was.

5   .... what happened, I've always been careful about where I leave my phone.

2 Match the halves of the questions. There is one ending you don't need.

1 What do you

2 Can you imagine

3 Can you guess what

A happened next?

B what I did after that?

C imagine it?

D think happened next?

3 Complete the expressions in the sentences.

1 S_ _d_ _ _y, I noticed that everyone was looking at me.

2 T_ _n I realised my mistake.

3 S_ _n after t_ _t, I got a message on my phone.

4 A l_t t_e l_t_r, the teacher asked to speak to me.

5 I_ the e_d, everything was fine.

4 Look at Exs 1, 2 and 3 again. Read the phrases and decide which exercise contains phrases in which the speaker

A introduces their story. ....

B describes the action in their story. ....

C includes the listener in their story. ....

D says what they remember. ....

5 🔊 3.6 Complete Carla's story with the correct words and phrases. Then listen and check.

can you guess   didn't really pay   I'm going to tell
looked down   suddenly   was looking at me
was using my phone   what happened

¹........................... you about something funny that happened to me in an English class. The teacher came in and asked us to take out our books. I ²........................... secretly under my desk, so I reached down and took my book out of my bag without looking. Then the teacher told us which page to turn to. Again, I was busy texting, so I ³........................... attention. ⁴..........................., the teacher said, 'Carla, can you read out the first paragraph on page 10?' I quickly opened my book at the right page and started reading. ⁵........................... what happened next? I continued reading until I realised that the teacher ⁶........................... angrily, and all my classmates were laughing. I ⁷........................... at the book in front of me. It was my history book, not my English book! After ⁸..........................., I'm always careful to check which books I'm taking out of my bag!

6 Tell Carla's story, and say what happened next. Record your answer.

Carla was in her English class. She wasn't listening carefully to the teacher because she was texting her friend. ....

7 🔊 3.7 Compare your recording with the one on track 3.7.

WRITING

a story

1 Match the strong adjectives (1–6) with their meanings (A–F).

1 freezing	**A** very tired
2 starving	**B** very good
3 delighted	**C** very cold
4 exhausted	**D** very good to eat
5 delicious	**E** very hungry
6 brilliant	**F** very happy

2 Replace the underlined words with a strong adjective from the box.

furious   huge   impossible   incredible   silent   tiny

1 Some of the questions in the test were <u>too difficult</u>!
....

2 I couldn't hear anything. The place was <u>very quiet</u>.
....

3 There was a <u>very big</u> rock in the middle of the road and we couldn't get past it. ....

4 She was holding a <u>very small</u> piece of gold between her fingers. ....

5 My dad was <u>very angry</u> with me because he thought I had lied to him. ....

6 We saw some <u>really good</u> things on our trip. ....

3 Read the task. Decide if the sentences (1–6) are true (T) or false (F).

> Your English teacher has asked you to write a story.
> Your story must begin with this sentence:
>
> **I got on the train and sat down.**
>
> Write your story in about **100 words**.

To get a good mark for your story:

1 it must start with the sentence in the task. ....

2 you should write about 100 words. ....

3 it must have a title. ....

4 it should use present tenses. ....

5 it should have a clear ending. ....

6 it should use interesting language. ....

4 Read the task in Ex 3 again. Then read three students' sentences to continue the story (1–3). Match each one with a description (A–C).

1 I got out my book, opened it and started to read.

2 I was really looking forward to my holiday.

3 It was a horrible, wet day and the train was cold and uncomfortable.

A gives a more detailed description ....

B continues with the action of the story ....

C gives background information ....

5 Read a student's story. Complete it with the extra phrases and sentences to make it more interesting.

A smiled and

B and we chatted all the way to London

C I felt really nervous

D I was so surprised

E Suddenly

I got on the train and sat down ¹........ . I was on my way to an interview for art college and in my bag was all my work. ²........ , the woman next to me asked, 'Are you going to London?' I told her all about art college, then she said, 'Can I see your work?' I showed her some of my pieces ³........ . When she got off the train, the woman ⁴........ said, 'You're very talented.'
An hour later, I walked into my interview. ⁵........ ! There was the woman from the train!

6 Read the task and plan your story.

> Your English teacher has asked you to write a story.
> Your story must begin with this sentence:
>
> **I took my phone out of my pocket and looked at the message.**
>
> Write your story in about **100 words**.

Who?	
When?	
Where?	
What?	
Ending	

7 🄴 Use your notes from Ex 6 to write your story. Write about 100 words.

UNIT CHECK

1 The bold adjectives are in the wrong sentences. Cross them out and write the correct adjectives.

1 Something that is **light** .... is very old.

2 Something that is **tiny** .... makes you feel frightened.

3 Something that is **huge** .... is worth a lot of money.

4 Something that is **scary** .... is very new.

5 Something that is **ancient** .... is boring.

6 Something that is **modern** .... doesn't weigh very much.

7 Something that is **valuable** .... is very small.

8 Something that is **dull** .... is very big.

2 Complete the adjectives in the blog post.

●●● <|>   🔍 🏠

No **great finds** today!

I love searching for old coins and other things that are buried under the ground. My new machine arrived yesterday, which was really ¹e_ _ _t_ _g! It's  much better than the old one and finds anything made of metal! It's also lighter, which makes it ²u_ _ _ _l for places where you have to walk quite a long way and carry everything! But, unfortunately, my visit to Warkley Woods wasn't brilliant. No ³g_ _ _ coins or jewellery today! It was quite ⁴d_ _ _ in the woods, so it was difficult to see where I was going. I found a few pieces of old farm tools – all quite ⁵o_ _ _n_ _y and nothing ⁶s_ _c_ _l or interesting, really. The only other thing I found (not with my machine) was an old ⁷w_ _ _ _n bucket. What can I use that for? Any ideas?

---

3 Read what the people say. Choose an adjective each person might use.

brand new   cute   excellent   funny   noisy   unusual

1 That's a great joke! ....

2 You got 10/10 in your test! ....

3 It isn't like most bikes because it's got three wheels. ....

4 Aah, look at those lovely baby ducks! ....

5 I only bought these shoes yesterday. ....

6 The music is so loud in here! ....

4 Complete the news stories with the correct past simple or past continuous form of the verbs in brackets.

The strangest emergency calls
Read about some of the strangest calls to the emergency services.

A 70-year-old woman ¹............................ (call) an ambulance because her wet clothes ²............................ (hang) outside to dry. She ³............................ (say) it was too cold for her to go out and bring them in!

The police ⁴............................ (receive) a call from a man who ⁵............................ (eat) a takeaway pizza. There were mushrooms on the pizza which he hadn't ordered, and he ⁶............................ (want) the police to make the takeaway restaurant give him another one.

Ella Grayson's son, Dan, ⁷............................ (lie) in bed one morning, although it was time to get up for school. Ella ⁸............................ (ask) the police to come and get him out of bed. The police ⁹............................ (give) her a fine for wasting their time!

5 Choose the correct words to complete the sentences.

1 I'm starving, but there's .... to eat here!

A nothing   B anything   C no one

2 I can't find my phone. Can .... see it?

A everyone   B anyone   C anything

3 There was a big fire and .... in the building was destroyed.

A anything   B everything   C nothing

4 .... ate the last piece of cake – who was it?

A Everyone   B Anyone   C Someone

5 Can .... be quiet for a moment, so I can make an announcement?

A everyone   B everything   C anyone

6 I'm bored – there isn't .... to do here!

A nothing   B something   C anything

REVIEW: UNITS 1–3

1 Complete the blog post with the correct article *a/an* or *the*, or no article (–).

Home | Recent Posts | Profile | Subscribe

Hi. I'm Yoshi and I live in
¹............................ apartment in
Tokyo with my family. Tokyo is the
capital of ²............................ Japan,
and it's ³............................ really
busy city – in fact it's one of the
busiest in ⁴............................ world.
So what is ⁵............................ life like
here? Well, I'm ⁶............................
student and I love it! There are lots of ⁷............................
things to do in different parts of ⁸............................ city, so
I'm never bored. ⁹............................ transport system is great,
so you definitely don't need ¹⁰............................ car to get
around. Why don't you come and visit one day?

2 Read what Maria from Spain says about visiting Tokyo. Choose the correct words to complete it.

Home | Recent Posts | Profile | Subscribe

There are ¹**a lot of / much** people
in Tokyo, of course, so most
places are really busy! There are
²**some / any** great places to visit,
and if you want ³**a few / a little**
time away from the busy streets,
you can go to one of the beautiful
gardens to enjoy ⁴**a few / a little**
minutes of quiet. I loved it, but it's difficult to do things
if you don't have ⁵**much / many** money. ⁶**All / Every** the
activities that I like doing are quite expensive. 😞

3 Complete the words in the notices.

① New exhibition of paintings by modern artists at the a_ _ g_ _ _ _ _ in the city centre. Starts this week.

② Please do not drop rubbish on the p_ _ _ _ _ _t. Use the b_ _s provided.

③ Sale at Jackson's d_ _ _ _ _ _ _ s_ _ _ all next week. 20% off clothes and household goods

④ For sale, two-bedroom flat in a large, modern a_ _ _ _ _ _ _ _ b_ _ _ _ . Great views of the city from all rooms! B_ _ s_ _ _ just outside with a regular service to the city centre.

4 Complete the posts with the correct present simple or present continuous form of the verbs in brackets.

What do you do outside school? Tell us about your hobbies.

ArtyJen
I ¹............................ (love) drawing! I ²............................
(always / carry) a pencil and paper around with
me so I can draw interesting things I see. At the
moment I ³............................ (try) to do a picture
of my dog, but he ⁴............................ (not sit) still
for me!

StrongSam
Climbing is the best sport! I ⁵............................ (go)
to the climbing wall every weekend, and
my uncle ⁶............................ (usually / take) me
outdoor climbing in the holidays. My arms
⁷............................ (get) stronger now, and my
uncle ⁸............................ (think) I may be ready to
try a big climb next summer!

5 Complete the advice with the correct form of the words and phrases in the box. There are two words or phrases you don't need.

> competition   encourage   go well   improve   practise
> results   skill   spend time

Riding a unicycle – advice for beginners

The first thing you need to know about riding a unicycle is that it isn't easy, and you need to **1**............................ a lot to get better. Aim for at least an hour a day. It really helps if other people **2**............................ you, especially at the beginning when it's really hard to stay on!

Focus on just riding forwards to start with. Don't try to do tricks too quickly. They need a lot of **3**............................ , and you can have some bad falls if you aren't ready.

Ask friends or family members to film you once a month, so you can see how you're **4**............................ each month.

5............................ watching videos online of other people riding unicycles. You can learn a lot by watching.

When you're ready, try taking part in a local **6**............................ . You might not win, but it will be good experience.

6 Complete the text with the correct form of the verbs.

Boy finds gold bar in lake

Last summer, teenager Aaron Barclay **1**............................ (go) on holiday with his family to Italy. On the first day of his holiday, the sun **2**............................ (shine) and it was hot, so he **3**............................ (decide) to go for a swim in the lake. While he **4**............................ (swim), he **5**............................ (notice) something bright under the water. He immediately **6**............................ (dive) down to the bottom and **7**............................ (find) a 500-gram gold bar! He **8**............................ (take) the gold to the local police station, but he doesn't know yet if he can keep the gold or not.

7 Complete the meanings with the correct words and their opposites.

> ancient   dark   dull   exciting   huge   light
> modern   ordinary   special   tiny

1 Something that is very old is .... The opposite is ....

2 Something that is boring is .... The opposite is ....

3 At night it is .... outside. The opposite is ....

4 Something that is normal and not different in any way is .... The opposite is ....

5 Something that is very small is .... The opposite is ....

8 **e** For each question, choose the correct answer.

What are the ingredients of the
perfect city?

There's a competition each year to find the world's most liveable city. But what do you need in the perfect city? Well, a good transport system is important, so you can travel around easily and not get **1**....... somewhere with no way of getting home. Good schools are important for young people so they know they can **2**....... good results in their exams. Another important ingredient is plenty of activities to **3**....... part in. These should include regular activities and also new things that catch your **4**....... and encourage you to have a go at something different. But it seems the most important thing is friends. There need to be places where people can go to **5**....... new friends when they first move to a city. And then plenty of interesting places where friends can **6**....... out together and chat.

	A	**B**	**C**	**D**
1	stuck	fixed	kept	tied
2	score	pass	get	find
3	have	take	do	try
4	ideas	mind	attention	thought
5	search	make	look	win
6	hang	meet	relax	spend

READING

1 Complete the names of the school subjects.

1 g_ _ _ _ _ _ _y
2 b_ _ _ _ _ _s
   s_ _ _ _ _s
3 h_ _ _ _ _y
4 a_ _
5 m_ _ _s

6 d_ _ _e
7 d_ _ _a
8 m_ _ _c
9 c_ _ _ _ _ _r
   s_ _ _ _ _s
10 s_ _ _ _ _e

2 Which subjects from Ex 1 are the students talking about?

Hans ....

> We're practising a song for the end of term concert.

Maria ....

> We sometimes go out and draw trees in the school gardens.

Helene ....

> I love learning about the mountains and rivers in foreign countries.

Alicia ....

> We're learning how to program and write code. It's fun!

Jorge ....

> I like acting out different situations.

3 Complete the collocation in the sentences with the correct alternatives.

1 My friend's parents are moving to Spain to **start** / **progress** a new business. I think it's a restaurant.
2 My dad's company is **making** / **doing** a lot of money so he's getting a raise.
3 They're **opening** / **delivering** a new sports centre in our town. Great!
4 My aunt has a book shop and she has good staff to help **plan** / **run** the business.
5 Before you ask the bank to lend you money, you need to **develop** / **think** a business plan.
6 It's important to learn how to **make** / **manage** a team well when you're working.

4 You are going to read a newsletter about new lessons. Look at the picture. What do you think the new lessons are in?

A journalism
B giving talks
C acting

5 **e** Read the newsletter. Choose the correct answers.

1 What is Sally Morris doing in the first paragraph?
   A introducing some new teachers
   B explaining how to get work in the future
   C talking about the value of some new lessons
   D reminding students to study hard
2 Sally talks about her own experience to show
   A how to give a good presentation.
   B why it's important to be confident.
   C that giving presentations can be difficult.
   D how interesting the topic can be.
3 In paragraph 3, Sally suggests that some speakers
   A are worried about giving talks.
   B are good at talking about familiar subjects.
   C are not interested in what they say.
   D are confused by their notes.
4 What does Sally say will happen at the end of the year?
   A Students will compete against people from other schools.
   B The world champion in giving presentations will visit their school.
   C One class will travel to Rome to watch some presentations.
   D Students will have three weeks to prepare for an international competition.

6 Match the phrasal verbs from the newsletter (1–6) with the meanings (A–F).

1	turn into	**A**	recover from
2	get over	**B**	move from doing one thing to another
3	go in for	**C**	change, become
4	figure out	**D**	learn
5	get into	**E**	become interested in
6	go on to	**F**	enter (a competition)

7 Use the phrasal verbs from Ex 6 to complete the sentences.

1 I'm trying to .... where this shop is – do you know?

2 Jamie knew he needed to .... his fear of flying before the holiday.

3 I didn't plan to .... Irish dancing, but I really love it!

4 We're all going to .... the contest, because the prizes are great.

5 When Cathy finishes school she wants to .... university.

6 My mum's small business is .... a huge company – she's very pleased.

New Year, new challenges!

Head teacher Sally Morris writes about plans for a new subject for the coming school year.

As your teachers have already told you, we are adding an interesting new subject to the timetable from next term. We all know that it's important to learn about science, languages, computer studies and so on. You'll need these in the future to find interesting jobs. However, we also need to learn other skills that can help us when we leave school and get work. We already have lessons on learning how to manage money, and years 10 and 11 also have business studies.

There is, however, something we *all* need to learn how to do well – and that's how to stand up and present ideas or information. And we need to get advice and practice in doing that as early as possible. So, from next term year 7s, 8s and 9s will have special lessons in giving presentations. Giving a good presentation is not easy. Sometimes people think you just do some research, make some notes, stand up in front of a group and talk. I, personally, have to do it all the time in my job and I can tell you it certainly isn't easy. But it's something you will need to do at some point in the future, so we are going to help you. Believe me, it's interesting and what's more, when you really get into it, it's great fun!

Some of you might be quite nervous about the idea of giving talks to groups of people. The lessons we've planned will help you get over those fears. You'll figure out where it's best to stand, where to look, and about body language. It's all about engaging your audience! And you'll get practice in talking about topics you know a lot about and some that might need researching. It's amazing how little tips can turn an anxious speaker who spends all the time reading from notes into a confident speaker who makes the whole audience interested in what he or she is saying.

There's a reward at the end of the year too. Three speakers, one each from years 7, 8 and 9, will go in for the National Junior Presentation Competition. We'll receive a list of topics two weeks before the competition to give some preparation time. The winners of the national competition will go on to compete in the international finals in Rome. The world champion might be right here at our school!

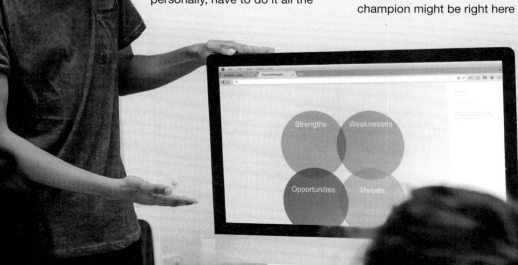

GRAMMAR

the future: plans and intentions

1 Decide if the sentences show an arrangement (A), an intention or plan (I) or something on a timetable / schedule (T).

1 We're having dinner at 7.30 this evening. ....

2 The test starts at 9.15. ....

3 The bus stops here in half an hour. ....

4 They're building a new science lab over there in September. ....

5 I'm going to learn some Italian before our summer holiday. ....

6 Danny is performing in the school play next weekend. ....

2 🔊 **4.1** Listen to the voicemail and tick the activities the girl mentions.

1 a journey by coach ☐

2 a break in a café ☐

3 a visit to an exhibition ☐

4 a walk round gardens ☐

5 eating sandwiches by the river ☐

6 a science talk ☐

7 a school project ☐

8 a school test ☐

3 🔊 **4.2** Listen to the voicemail again and complete the sentences.

1 The coach .... school at 8.30.

2 We .... round the new robotics exhibition in a group in the morning.

3 We .... all .... sandwiches.

4 We .... somewhere outside by the river.

5 Amy and Ben .... the workshop on designing robots.

6 Miss Manners .... us a mini project.

7 The coach .... back to school at 5.15.

4 Form new similar sentences using the words in brackets.

1 I'm going to watch TV this evening. (my sister)

....

2 The new shopping centre opens on 16th August. (not)

....

3 I'm meeting Beth after school at the café. (you ?)

....

4 The new maths teacher starts next Monday. (When ?)

....

5 I'm going to stay in bed late tomorrow. (not)

....

6 We're having a geography test later today. (not)

....

5 Read the blog and decide if each sentence is an arrangement, an intention or part of a schedule. Then complete each gap with the present simple, present continuous or *going to* form of the verb in brackets.

●●● ◁▷   🔍 🏠

| HOME | NEW POSTS | ABOUT | 🔍 |

Some of you have asked me about school while I'm making a film. OK. Well — it's hard! Child actors like me must have 15 hours school a week, but when you're filming you can't go to normal school! I have a private teacher who teaches me on location. Like today, for example. They **1** .... (film) one of the scenes I'm in after breakfast this morning. That usually lasts an hour or maybe an hour and a half. Then, according to my study timetable, at 11.00 I **2** .... (have) a lesson in my room. I **3** .... (ask) my studio teacher to check through some questions I've got about yesterday's lessons. We've got less than half an hour before filming **4** .... (start) again at 11.20! We **5** .... (stop) for lunch at 12.30, like every day. Then if I'm not too tired, my parents **6** .... (drive) me to another studio in town to audition for another film. That **7** .... (start) filming next year! My studio teacher **8** .... (come round) again this evening at some point and give me a maths lesson. After that I **9** .... (do) some revising because I know I **10** .... (have) a test early tomorrow morning — that's before I **11** .... (go) into make-up at 8.00! Every day is different! But I love this life! I **12** .... (not / do) it forever but it's fun right now!

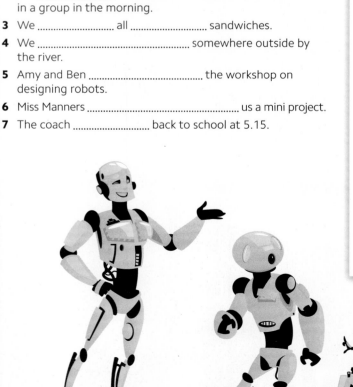

VOCABULARY

ways of learning

1 🔊 **4.3 Complete the notes with the correct prepositions. Listen and check.**

Notes to self!

1 Don't sit .... for a long time when you're working. Stand .... and move .... after twenty minutes.

2 Make .... your mind when to do your homework and then DO it!

3 Tell Katy .... if she interrupts you while you're working.

4 Don't hand .... your homework late. The teacher doesn't like it.

5 Don't worry if the teacher crosses .... things in your homework. Learn from it.

6 Note .... exactly what the teacher wants you to do for homework or you'll do the wrong things!

7 If something's difficult get .... and walk .... for a bit. Then settle .... again and it will be easier.

2 Complete the conversations with the correct verbs.

get   give   have   make   take (x2)

1 A: I think you're really good on the guitar!
B: Thanks. Here – why don't you .... a go?

2 A: I keep getting bad marks for my essays.
B: .... my advice and check them through carefully before you hand them in.

3 A: I'm sure I won't be good at skateboarding!
B: Just .... it a try! You never know.

4 A: Which university is your brother going to?
B: He needs to .... good grades and then he's going to Cambridge!

5 A: I'm worried about the audition for the school play.
B: Oh, ... a chance – it's not a problem if you don't get a part, is it?

6 A: I hope my brother doesn't .... a mistake in his driving test.
B: I'm sure he's going to be fine!

3 Choose the correct answers to complete the post.

You know how sometimes it's hard to learn in class if some students don't settle [1] .... and the teacher is always [2] .... people off? Well, today in my art class absolutely everyone was quiet and concentrating hard – we used VR and it was amazing! We each had a headset and suddenly I was at the Rodin museum in Paris! Wow! With VR you can move [3] .... the garden and look at all the sculptures. It's OK to take notes from a teacher in class but sometimes I don't note [4] .... everything and I often [5] .... mistakes. With VR you can go back and look again and again, from every side! Before I tried I wasn't sure about it. Some people say that it can make you feel a bit sick. But if you get the chance, [6] .... my advice and give it a [7] .... It really is incredible and I know I'm going to [8] .... good grades in art this year!

1 A up	**B** out	**C** down	**D** off
2 A saying	**B** doing	**C** speaking	**D** telling
3 A on	**B** around	**C** by	**D** at
4 A over	**B** down	**C** for	**D** out
5 A give	**B** take	**C** make	**D** do
6 A get	**B** take	**C** listen	**D** check
7 A do	**B** see	**C** go	**D** think
8 A make	**B** bring	**C** do	**D** get

Extend

4 Which classes are the students talking about?

biology   chemistry   economics   IT   photography   technology

1 In .... we took pictures in the school garden.

2 In .... we mixed some things together and they went bright green.

3 In .... we created different apps.

4 In .... we learned about the world's money markets.

5 In .... we learned about how plants grow.

6 In .... we learned about how a car engine works.

LISTENING

1 🔊 4.4 **Listen to five conversations. Which conversations (1–5) mention the topics A–G. There are two extra topics.**

A learning online ....

B a celebration ....

C using dictionaries ....

D friends at school ....

E a school in a different country ....

F revising for tests ....

G long lessons ....

2 🔊 4.5 **Listen again. For each conversation, circle the two words you hear.**

1 timetable listening classmates friend

2 Italian app pronunciation travelling

3 subjects homework modern popular

4 party friends science classroom

5 sport city village discussions

3 **e** 🔊 4.6 **Listen again and choose the correct answers.**

1 You will hear two friends talking about learning at home. What would the girl enjoy if she learned at home?

   A choosing which subjects to study

   B staying in bed late

   C making a lot of progress

2 You will hear two friends talking about a language course. How does the girl feel?

   A surprised how quickly she's learning

   B confused by the teacher's instructions

   C nervous about speaking the language on holiday

3 You will hear a girl telling her friend about an unusual school. Why is the school unusual?

   A The buildings are a strange colour.

   B The classroom design is unusual.

   C The students learn different things.

4 You will hear two friends talking about a visit to their old school. What are they both looking forward to?

   A meeting their old teachers

   B seeing their old friends

   C looking at their old classrooms

5 You will hear two friends talking about their fathers' schools. What was true for both their fathers?

   A they went to the same school

   B they were in large classes

   C they had to be quiet in class

the future: predictions

4 **Complete the sentences with the correct alternatives.**

1 I'm certain we **'ll / might** get a lot of geography homework this weekend.

2 We **'ll / might** get a new maths teacher next term. I think Miss Kenny is leaving.

3 We've got an English test tomorrow. I know I **'ll / might** fail it! I didn't revise.

4 We definitely **won't / might not** get our homework back before next week because the teacher's in London for a meeting today and tomorrow.

5 You **'ll / might** love New York. My friend went there last year and she said it's an amazing place.

6 There aren't many students in the photography club now so it **will / might** stop soon. I hope not. It's a great club.

5 **Complete the dialogue with** *will* **or** *might***.**

What subjects do you think students
1 .... learn at schools in the future?

That's a difficult question! I'm pretty sure they
2 .... still learn maths and IT. But I don't know about art and drama and music. They
3 .... not be on the timetable in the future.

I agree, we **4** .... definitely still study technology and computers. I'm sure everyone
5 .... start learning to program at a very early age. But you **6** .... be right about arts subjects. Students **7** .... do that in clubs or at home. What do you think? I'm sure languages **8** .... be important but it's possible that everyone in the world
9 .... just speak one language!

I love arts, but I think you're right! I just hope the one language **10** .... be one I speak!

6 **Write some predictions about what careers or jobs your classmates** *will* **or** *might* **have.**

1 David will definitely be a teacher. He loves telling people about different things.

2 ....

....

3 ....

....

4 ....

....

5 ....

....

SPEAKING

1 Which student comments about the exam picture task are true (T) and which are false (F)?

1 You are given a photo and you have to talk about it with your partner. ....
2 You talk about two photos on your own. ....
3 You talk about one photo on your own. ....
4 You describe a photo and only say what you're sure is happening. ....
5 You say what you can see in a photo and make some guesses. ....
6 You talk for about two minutes. ....

2 🔊 4.7 Look at photo A and listen to the examiner's instruction and the student's answer. The student makes three guesses about where the people in the photo are. What are they?

1 ....
2 ....
3 ....

3 🔊 4.8 Listen again and complete the student's answer with the correct words.

OK. Yes, this photo ¹.......................... some friends together. There ².......................... three people – two girls and a boy. They ³.......................... on the grass and they ⁴.......................... . They ⁵.......................... relaxed and happy together. We can see two of their faces, but one girl is facing ⁶.......................... from the camera. I think they ⁷.......................... in a park. Or maybe they're at ⁸........................... . There is a big beautiful building behind them – I ⁹.......................... what it is, but ¹⁰.......................... it's their school. Or they ¹¹.......................... older and this is their university. Yes, I think that's ¹².......................... right.

4 Look at photo B and read the task.

'Your photo shows people talking. Please tell us what you can see in the photo.'

Make some notes about:

1 where the people are
2 what they are doing
3 what they are wearing and why
4 how they might be feeling

5 🔵 Read the task in Ex 4 again. Then record yourself. Listen to your recording. Did you talk about all of the notes you made in Ex 4?

6 Complete the sentences with the correct words.

about	because	check	could	fancy
idea	perhaps	see	sounds	wait

A: Do you ¹.......................... going to the concert in the park this weekend? It's on Saturday and Sunday afternoons.

B: I'd love to, but I can't go on Saturday ².......................... I've got a swimming competition.

A: OK. What ³.......................... Sunday? We ⁴.......................... meet at the entrance at about 11.30?

B: That ⁵.......................... good, but I need to ⁶.......................... with Simon. He's coming round to see me. ⁷.......................... we could all go?

A: Great ⁸.......................... !

B: Cool. ⁹.......................... you on Sunday!

A: I can't ¹⁰.......................... !

WRITING

an email

1 Which of these statements are true about the exam writing email task? Write *true*, or correct the wrong information.

1 You have to write the answer to another person's email.

....

2 You need to answer some questions in the email and make some comments.

....

3 There are three points you have to include.

....

4 You should write about 200 words.

....

2 Which words or phrases go at the beginning (B) or at the end (E) of an informal email?

1 See you soon. ....
2 How are things? ....
3 Hope you're well. ....
4 Write soon. ....
5 Hi there, ...
6 Bye for now. ....
7 How are you? ....
8 Hello ....
9 Great to hear from you. ....
10 Hi! ....
11 Thanks for writing. ....
12 Hope to hear from you soon. ....

3 Lily is going with some other students to visit another school. Read her email to a student at the school. Then look at the notes you are going to use to reply. Match points 1–4 with the notes in the email.

1 hockey in afternoon – don't bring anything – equipment here – English literature, maths.
2 yes – 15th March
3 great to meet you!
4 watching film of *Romeo and Juliet* – suggest read summary of story?

Hi,

How are things? We're coming to your school next Tuesday. I can't wait! It will be so good to meet you and see your school. → ① *Yes!*

What's happening on Tuesday? Should I bring anything special – like sports stuff? → ② *tell her*

And about the lessons. Have you got any advice about any reading or preparation I need to do? → ③ *advise*

Some students from your class are coming on a return visit to our school next month. Will you come too? I think you'll enjoy it! What's the date? → ④ *yes – give date*

See you on Tuesday!

Lily

---

4 Plan your email to Lily. Use the table to make notes for each of the four points.

Email beginning	
Note 1	
Note 2	
Note 3	
Note 4	
Email ending	

5 **e** Use your notes to write your email to Lily. Write about 100 words.

6 Read your email and check that:

1 you've written about 100 words. ☐
2 you've used an informal beginning and ending. ☐
3 you've answered all the points. ☐
4 your spelling is correct. ☐
5 you've used good paragraphing and punctuation. ☐
6 your grammar is accurate. ☐

UNIT CHECK

1
Complete the puzzle with the names of subjects using the key words (1–8). What subject is spelled out in the purple boxes?

1 countries, rivers
2 pictures, black and white, colour
3 human body, plants, trees
4 singing, guitar, piano
5 kings and queens
6 chemistry, physics
7 money, companies
8 numbers, adding, 2+2 = 4

1 g   p
2 p
3 b
4 m
5 h
6 s
7 e
8 m

2
Complete the phrasal verbs in the sentences with the correct prepositions.

1 The teacher told me .... today for using my phone in class.
2 We found .... in class today that we're having a test on Friday.
3 Pete repaired my bicycle this morning and I'll try it .... later.
4 In the exercise we had to cross .... the incorrect answers.
5 When do we need to hand .... our maths homework?
6 Can you go .... the instructions for the project with me again, please?

3
Make sentences by matching sentence parts 1–6 with A–F.

1 You need to make up ....
2 My brother finds it difficult to take ....
3 At the moment we're doing ....
4 It's hard but you should give ....
5 If you make ....
6 I have to work very hard to get ....

A advice from anyone.
B good grades in biology.
C a mistake, just try again.
D it a try.
E a really interesting project in science.
F your mind about your plans for the weekend.

4
Complete the collocations in the sentences with the correct alternatives.

1 My friend's parents **worked / started** a business in Manchester.
2 Have you **developed / managed** a business plan yet?
3 You need to be organised to be able to **start / manage** a team well.
4 The business is **losing / running** money, so they'll have to sell it.
5 My uncle is having problems **running / opening** the business by himself so it isn't doing very well.

5
Complete the email with the correct form of the verbs in brackets.

Hi

What [1]........................... (you / do) this weekend? Have you got any plans?
I [2]........................... (go) to the cinema with Dave and Karen on Saturday afternoon. We [3]........................... (meet) outside at 2.15. Do you fancy coming with us? The film [4]........................... (start) at 2.30 and [5]........................... (finish) at 4.15. Then we [6]........................... (do) some shopping. The shops [7]........................... (not / close) until 6.30 on Saturday so there'll be lots of time to spend some money! I [8]........................... (swim) in a competition next Saturday so this is my last shopping day before our holiday! I'm [9]........................... (spend) a lot of my mum's money!

Let me know, and maybe see you there?

Love Beth

6
Complete the sentences with the correct form of *will, won't, might* or *might not*.

1 I'm not sure about the train times so I'm afraid I .... be late.
2 It .... definitely be hot on the beach, so wear a hat!
3 The tickets for the concert .... cost at least £15 because the band is very popular.
4 I know I .... pass the exam because I only answered ten questions.
5 My cousin .... open a café in town but he's worried he .... have enough money.

READING

1 Complete the article with the correct words.

accessories   average   expert
fancy   patterns   slogans

How to find

your
style

It can be difficult to find the right look for you. Adam Fox, an ¹........................... on fashion and style, offers some advice.

"

The first thing is to know your own body. Most people aren't an ²........................... size, so not every style suits them. Choose clothes that fit your shape. Don't let clever advertising ³........................... persuade you to buy something that isn't right for you. If you ⁴........................... buying something different, make sure you try it on and see if it looks good. Choose your mix of colours carefully. Also, remember that some people look better in plain colours, and some people look better in ⁵........................... . Finally, choose your ⁶..........................., like bags, watches and rings, carefully – they can make a big difference to the way you look.

"

2 Read about four young people who are interested in a 'style experience'. Choose the correct answer.

The four young people

A are all unhappy with the way they look and want to change the way they dress.

B all want a style experience to change their look or change how they feel about their appearance.

C all want to get advice on fashion from fashion designers and buy new clothes they can feel confident in.

3 **e** Read the advertisements on page 41 for six style experiences. Decide which experience is best for each person.

Lily ....   Mark ....   Amy ....   Paul ....

Lily

Lily loves expensive clothes and would like to look really stylish by improving her hair and make-up. She doesn't want to buy any clothes but wants a half-day experience, with something to help her remember it. ....

Mark

Mark doesn't have much money so doesn't want to buy designer clothes. He wants advice on the latest fashions and help with trying on and buying clothes for different occasions in shops in his local shopping centre. ....

Amy

Amy has plenty of clothes so doesn't want to buy any more. She wants advice on which of her clothes **match** and look good on her. She'd also like advice on her hairstyle and accessories. ....

Paul

Paul has plenty of clothes, but he wants advice on how to improve his appearance by getting in shape and becoming fitter. He'd like to share the experience with some friends. ....

Our top style experiences

A The new you

Enjoy a morning appointment with a top hair **stylist**, plus either a make-up expert or fitness coach. After lunch, our fashion expert will use the latest software to give general advice on what colours and styles will suit you, and the best designer brands for you to wear. Individual bookings only — no groups.

B Personal style

Westhill Department Store has a fantastic collection of informal and special occasion clothes from top fashion brands. In this half-day experience, our style expert will show you why it's worth spending extra to look good, and how to stand out with the right accessories. Suitable for groups or individuals. Please note, you are expected to buy at least two items.

C Top tips

Do you have a wardrobe full of clothes but never feel you look good? Working individually with you at home, our style expert will show you how to **save** money by putting your clothes together in different ways to produce different looks. They'll also show how belts, bags, jewellery and a small change of hairstyle can help you really stand out.

D Look great!

Forget about changing your hair or buying more clothes. We believe that the right look comes from the inside and needn't **cost** a lot of money. In this three-hour experience, our health experts and trainers will work with you to create a diet and exercise plan that will make you feel great about yourself, whatever you're wearing. Groups welcome.

E Fashion friends

Our style expert will spend a morning at the shopping centre with you, showing you what's in fashion this year for both **formal** and relaxed situations. They'll help you find clothes that look good together and suit your body shape, so you can create your own personal look. Ideal if you want to look good at **reasonable** prices! No groups.

F Fabulous you

See how it feels to be a top fashion model for an afternoon. Our hair and make-up experts will get you looking your best, then you'll wear some of the latest collections from top designers in a photo session with a professional fashion photographer. You won't believe how great you look, and you'll have the photos to prove it!

---

4 Look again at the advertisements and the descriptions of the four young people. Match the words in bold with their meanings.

1 suitable for wearing when you go out to a special event
....

2 someone who helps people to look good ....

3 not too expensive ....

4 to look nice together ....

5 the amount of money you have to pay for something
....

6 to spend less money, so you have some to keep ....

5 Complete the sentences with the answers from Ex 4.

1 Jana trusted her .... to make her look fabulous.

2 The coat was beautiful but it .... too much for Ella.

3 James asked his parents for a hat to .... his favourite scarf.

4 The new shop was popular because of its .... prices.

5 It's always easier to .... money if you have a goal you're aiming for.

6 It's important to wear .... clothes if you go for a job interview.

GRAMMAR

making comparisons

1 🔊 **5.1 Choose the correct comparative and superlative forms to complete the conversations. Listen and check.**

A Is this an old photo of you?

B Yes. My hair was **¹shorter / shortest** then, so I look quite different.

A It looks **²the nicest / nicer** now that it's long.

B Thanks.

A Are you going to buy those trainers?

B Are you joking? They're the **³more expensive / most expensive** ones in the shop! I'm sure I can find some in another shop that are **⁴better / the best** value.

A What's the **⁵worse / worst** piece of clothing you've ever bought?

B Some bright pink boots! They're also the **⁶most practical / least practical** thing I've ever bought, because they were really uncomfortable!

A Why do you always wear jeans?

B I guess I just feel **⁷more comfortable / the most comfortable** in jeans than in other clothes. You love wearing unusual clothes, but I'm **⁸more adventurous / less adventurous** than you, and I prefer to wear things that I'm comfortable in. We're all different!

2 Choose the correct words to complete the forum posts.

What **crazy things** have you done to try to look good?

Tell us your stories!

GinaPP

I once decided to colour my hair, to make it **¹**........ . Unfortunately, I wasn't **²**........ about watching the time. I left the colour on for **³**........ , and my hair turned yellow!

Jon55

I saw a really nice jumper in a second-hand shop. I thought it was **⁴**........ the clothes in the big stores, but obviously **⁵**........ When I showed it to my friend later, he said, 'That's my dad's old jumper!'

SaraG

I once borrowed a really cool dress from a friend, to go to a party, but I'm **⁶**........ her, so unfortunately, it was **⁷**........ . I bought some shoes with high heels to solve the problem and was really pleased that I felt **⁸**........ to wear them. But I fell over as I walked into the party!

	A	**B**	**C**
1	as light	lighter	too light
2	less careful	as careful	careful enough
3	too long	long enough	the longest
4	nice enough	nicer	as nice as
5	as expensive	less expensive	not expensive enough
6	not as tall as	taller	not tall enough
7	long enough	as long	too long
8	too confident	confident enough	as confident

3 Complete the second sentence so it has a similar meaning to the first. Use the word in brackets.

1 These shoes aren't big enough for me.
These shoes .... for me. (small)

2 I'm less interested in clothes than my brother!
I'm not .... my brother. (as)

3 All the other coats are more expensive than this one.
This is .... coat. (least)

4 Your appearance isn't as important as your health.
Your health is .... your appearance. (important)

5 I prefer more adventurous clothes than these ones.
These clothes .... for me. (aren't)

6 Small shops are more expensive than big stores.
Big stores .... small shops. (as)

4 Complete the blog post with one word in each gap.

Don't worry – be happy!

Let's be honest, we all have at least one worry about our appearance. Maybe you think you aren't thin **¹**........................... to wear certain clothes, or maybe when you look in the mirror you think that your body isn't **²**........................... strong and fit as you'd like it to be. But is your appearance really **³**........................... most important thing in your life? NO! I think it's time we all agreed to accept ourselves as we are and stop worrying. OK, so you might be a bit taller **⁴**........................... you'd like, or maybe your nose really is **⁵**........................... big to look perfect – both of these are true for me! – but these things are definitely **⁶**........................... important than the really big things in life, like spending time with friends and having fun!

VOCABULARY

describing appearance

1 Complete the puzzle. Then use the shaded letters to make a word to complete sentence 6.

1			l			
2				s		
3			k			
4				k		
5		w				

1 You keep your money in this.
2 You wear these to help you see better.
3 A lot of people carry their school books in this.
4 These appear on my face in the summer!
5 A general word for things like rings and necklaces.
6 My best friend and I both wear .... !

2 🔊 5.2 Complete the descriptions with the correct words. Listen and check.

> I guess I'm quite ¹s_ _ _t because I'm only 1m 60 ²t_ _ _. I've got ³f_ _ _ hair, although I'd prefer to have really dark hair! I love clothes, but I don't often wear ⁴m_ _ _-_p.

> I'm ⁵a_ _r_ _e h_ _ _ _t, not very tall or very short. I'm also quite ⁶s_ _m because I do a lot of sport. I've got ⁷l_ _g hair which is also ⁸c_ _ _y. It's annoying because it's difficult to style.

> Most of my friends are taller than me because I'm quite ⁹s_ _ _l for my ¹⁰a_ _, although I hope I'll keep growing.

3 Complete the questions about Tom.

1 A .... Tom?
   B He's fifteen. His birthday was on Saturday.

2 A What .... Tom .... like?
   B He's quite tall and he's got freckles.

3 A .... look like?
   B Definitely his brother. They've got the same eyes.

4 A What .... like?
   B He's really funny, and very friendly.

5 A What .... like?
   B He likes music and he loves football!

4 Read the article and choose the correct answers.

WHY DO WE ALL WANT WHAT WE HAVEN'T GOT?

It's strange that almost everyone is unhappy with their body in some way. People who are ¹........ height want to be taller, while tall people want to be shorter. People who ²........ glasses hate them, while others think that glasses would make them ³........ more intelligent. In my case, it's hair. I have ⁴........ hair but I dream of having straight hair. Why? According to psychologists, we pay attention to things to do with ⁵........ , like height and hair, when really we want to change our personality – we want to be funnier, braver or more confident. And we can learn these things, with some training.

1	A basic	B acceptable	C average	D common
2	A carry	B wear	C keep	D take
3	A show	B give	C look	D see
4	A curly	B round	C large	D wide
5	A fashion	B style	C appearance	D design

Extend

5 Read what Carrie says about a shopping experience. Match the underlined words with the meanings.

> ● ● ● ◀ ▶   🔍 🏠
>
> I went shopping last week and found a really nice jumper. I thought it would ¹go with my new jeans, and it was quite cheap too, so I thought it was a ²bargain. It looked the right size, so I ³paid for it and took it home. When I ⁴put it on, I found that it was ⁵damaged – there was a hole in one sleeve. Can you believe it? Luckily, I still had the ⁶receipt, so I took it back to the shop and changed it.

A gave the money for ....
B broken or not perfect ....
C look nice with another piece of clothing ....
D a piece of paper you get from a shop showing what you bought ....
E put a piece of clothing on your body ....
F something you buy for less than the price you expect ....

5 Get the look!

LISTENING

1 🔊 5.3 You will hear a woman giving information about a school fashion evening. Listen and choose the correct answers.

1 The speaker is giving information **at a school / on the radio.**

2 The speaker is talking about a **past / future** event.

3 The speaker wants people to **attend / take part in and attend** the event.

2 ⓔ 🔊 5.4 Listen again and complete the information. Write one or two words, a number, a date or a time.

Highbury School — Fashion Event

The date of the fashion event is **¹**...........................

The fashion show starts at **²**...........................

Students can get advice from a **³**........................... on the night.

Place where models should meet Mrs Daniels on Friday: **⁴**...........................

After the show, people can buy drinks and snacks in the **⁵**........................... .

Students can sell their old clothes and **⁶**........................... at the event.

3 🔊 5.5 Complete sentences 1–5 from the audio with the correct words from the box. Listen and check.

magnificent	reduce	refreshments	second-hand	spectacular

1 We've already sold 200 tickets, which is ....

2 The main event is our .... fashion show.

3 They've all promised to .... their prices for the night.

4 After the show, we're serving ....

5 Don't forget the .... clothes stalls.

4 Match the words from Ex 3 with their meanings.

1 to make something lower in amount ....

2 already owned and worn by someone ....

3 amazing to watch or look at ....

4 food and drink ....

5 very good ....

much/a lot/a bit + comparative, *not quite as … as*

5 Choose the correct words to complete the blog post.

SCHOOL FASHION EVENING

What a night! I have now done my first ever show as a fashion model! Before the show, I was **¹a lot / quite** more nervous than I expected. I could hardly put my clothes on, my hands were shaking so much! The clothes were amazing – **²much / lot** more colourful than I usually wear. I felt like a celebrity! Walking out in front of the audience was actually OK – it wasn't **³much / quite** as scary as I thought it would be. Going across the stage was fine but getting up and down the steps was a bit **⁴as / more** difficult because of the high heels I was wearing. I'm so glad I did it, though. I feel much **⁵confident / more confident** than before, and I know I'm not **⁶as famous as / more famous** the models in the fashion magazines yet, but since I took part one or two people have recognised me and said I did well!

6 Read the comments on the blog post in Ex 5. Complete them with one word in each space.

1 Well done! I don't think I could do that, but I guess I'm not as brave .... you!

2 I was in a fashion show once, and I think I was much more nervous .... you – I fell over as I came onto the stage!

3 Can you imagine how the top models feel? The shows they do are .... lot bigger than yours!

4 You're lucky your school organises events like this! The events at my school are .... quite as exciting as this!

5 I'm glad you enjoyed the experience. You will definitely feel a bit .... confident next time!

SPEAKING

1 Look at photo A and read the sentences. Which are describing the photo (D) and which are making guesses (G) about it?

1 The photo shows two young men. ....

2 Maybe they're friends, or brothers. ....

3 They're looking at some clothes in a shop. ....

4 I think it might be a sports shop. ....

5 One of the men is holding a white T-shirt. ....

6 He looks happy. ....

7 They probably want to buy some new clothes. ....

8 The other man is looking at some shorts. ....

2 🔊 5.6 Look at photo B. Choose the correct words to complete the guesses. Listen and check.

"I can see two people. One is a girl and the other **¹is probably / probably is** her mother. The girl **²looks / is looking** about 12 years old, and she's wearing a light-coloured top. They're in a clothes shop, and they're looking at some jeans. The mother is holding the jeans and the girl is looking at them. I think **³might / maybe** the girl wants to buy some new jeans and her mother is helping her choose them. The mother **⁴looks / looks like** happy because she's smiling. The girl isn't smiling a lot, but she looks interested in the jeans. I think she **⁵might / maybe** like them, so her mother **⁶probably will / will probably** buy them for her."

3 Look at photo B again. Decide if the sentences are true or false.

1 The girl is on the right.

2 The girl is standing next to her mother.

3 The two people are in the middle of the photo.

4 There are some clothes hanging up in front of the girl.

5 There are some white T-shirts on the right of the photo.

6 There are some clothes hanging up on the left, behind the girl.

4 Complete the things a customer might say in a shop using the correct word from the box. There are two words you don't need.

changing   fit   have   looking   suit   take   try   want

1 I'm .... for some brown boots.

2 I like this jumper. Can I .... it on?

3 Where are the .... rooms?

4 These jeans are very comfortable and they .... really well.

5 These shoes are really nice. I'll .... them.

6 Can I .... a bag, please?

5 Read what the sales assistant says and choose the best response.

1 Hi, can I help you?

  A Of course, no problem.

  B Yes, I'm looking for a black jacket.

2 What size are you?

  A Small, I think.

  B We've got this one in your size.

3 Would you like to try it on?

  A Of course. The changing rooms are over there.

  B Yes, please. Where are the changing rooms?

4 Is the jacket any good for you?

  A Yes, it fits perfectly. I'll take it.

  B Of course. Here it is. Would you like a bag?

5 That's £64 to pay, please.

  A Here you are.

  B Thank you. Here's your change.

WRITING

a review

1 Choose the correct connectors to complete the sentences from product reviews.

1 This tablet is really good quality **and / but** not too expensive.

2 The sunglasses looked really good, **because / so** I ordered some online.

3 I needed a new phone **but / because** I'd lost my old one.

4 I wanted to buy a fitness tracker, **so / but** I didn't want to spend too much money.

5 I got some money for my birthday, **so / but** I decided to buy this computer game.

2 Link these sentences from product reviews. Use *and*, *but*, *because* or *so*.

1 The shoes were a real bargain. I bought them.

....

2 I bought some new trainers. My old ones were too small.

....

3 I like the big screen on this phone. The camera is excellent too.

....

4 It's a really cool drinks bottle. It isn't big enough.

....

3 Read the task. Then complete the paragraph plan with the correct words.

Best and worst buys!

Tell us about something you've bought recently.

> What's good about it?
> What's not so good?
> Would you recommend it to other people?
> Why/Why not?
> Share your experiences with us!

---

description   negative   positive   recommendation

Paragraph 1
brief ¹ .... *of the product and where I bought it*
Paragraph 2
² .... *points about the product (good price, nice style)*
Paragraph 3
³ .... *points about the product (not easy to use, not good quality)*
Paragraph 4
Conclusion and ⁴ ....

4 Read a product review of a game controller. Choose the correct words to complete it.

I bought the ZXC game controller last week. My old one was six years old, so I wanted something newer and better.

The ¹**best / worst** thing about it is that it's comfortable to hold, and you can reach all the controls easily. Another fantastic ²**feature / problem** is that it's wireless, so you don't have to connect it to your computer.

The only ³**worst thing / problem** is that some of the buttons don't work well together. If you're holding the direction button down, the option button doesn't always work very quickly. It's OK for some games, but not for driving games, which I love.

⁴**All in all / All for all**, this is a nice controller, but I ⁵**shouldn't / wouldn't** recommend it because of the problem with the controls. There are plenty of better controllers available.

5 Complete these sentences from other reviews of the ZXC game controller. There are two words you don't need.

---

advice   good   help   review   shame   whole

---

1 A .... thing is that it's strong, so it won't break if you drop it.

2 It's a .... that some of the controls fail when you're in the middle of a game.

3 On the .... , I don't think it's a good buy.

4 My .... is to choose a controller with more reliable controls.

6 Look at the task in Ex 3 again and choose something you have bought recently. Plan your review. Use the paragraph plan in Ex 3.

Paragraph 1

....

Paragraph 2

....

Paragraph 3

....

Paragraph 4

....

7 **e** Use your notes and write your product review. Write about 100 words.

UNIT CHECK

1 Complete the words in the sentences.

1 I lost my w............................ with all my money in it!

2 I can see much better with my new g............................ .

3 I think little kids with f............................ on their face look really cute!

4 I need a big b............................ to carry all my books to school.

5 It's worth having b............................ when you're young, so you have great teeth when you're older.

6 We aren't allowed to wear rings or any other j............................ at school.

7 Some girls feel more confident when they wear m............................ , but I prefer my face to look natural.

2 Complete the descriptions with the correct words. There are two words in each group that you don't need.

1 I've got short, ... hair and I'm quite .... for my age, but everyone tells me not to worry because I'll grow as I get older.

> curly   long   small   tall

2 I'm 1m 65 .... and I've got long, ... hair.

> high   small   straight   tall

3 I'm .... height and I've got short .... hair.

> average   big   fair   small

4 I'm quite .... – only 1m 59, and I'm quite .... too.

> curly   short   slim   straight

5 I've got .... , black hair and lots of .... on my face.

> fair   freckles   glasses   long

3 Match the questions (1–6) with their answers (A–F).

1 How old is Ben?

2 What does he look like?

3 How tall is he?

4 Who does he look like?

5 What is he like?

6 What does he like?

A Quite tall and slim.

B Really good fun!

C Sixteen.

D Music and sport.

E He's about 1m 64.

F Just like his dad!

4 Complete the article with the correct words. Use the comparative or superlative form of the adjectives, or less / least, too, enough or (not) as … as.

NO MORE TRYING CLOTHES ON!

I'm not good at choosing clothes. Things never seem to look ¹............................ (nice) on me as they do hanging up in the shop. The style I choose might be ²............................ (short) for me, or I might take my usual size only to find it isn't ³............................ (big) once I get into the changing rooms. Or, more likely, I find that once I put something on that I just look ⁴............................ (amazing) than I imagined! The ⁵............................ (bad) thing about the experience is all that getting dressed and undressed! So I'm really happy that some shops now have the technology to do it for me, and I can sit at a computer screen and put as many clothes as I want onto a model of myself. It's definitely ⁶............................ (fast) than trying on lots of different clothes in changing rooms, and it's ⁷............................ (interesting) too, because you can see yourself from all sides, and get a really good idea of what you'll look like in the clothes. And the ⁸............................ (good) thing is, there's no limit to the number of things you can try on!

5 Complete the second sentence so it has a similar meaning to the first. Use the words in brackets.

1 This new game is much better than the old one.
This new game .... the old one. (lot)

2 My brother's a bit taller than me.
I'm not .... my brother. (quite)

3 The jacket isn't quite as expensive as the coat.
The coat is .... the jacket. (bit)

4 The new shopping centre is a lot bigger than the old one.
The old shopping centre was .... the new one. (much)

5 It was a bit colder yesterday than it is today.
Today is .... yesterday. (quite)

6 The great outdoors

READING

1 Complete the sentences with the correct adjectives.

> colourful   empty   peaceful   social   wild

1 It's very .... sitting in the garden with just the sound of the birds.

2 Some roads in the USA go across wide .... areas of land, with no trees or houses.

3 Our park is a very .... place and lots of people meet there to chat.

4 The countryside near my home is quite .... with lots of trees and bushes but there are some interesting walks and paths.

5 I like .... gardens with lots of different flowers.

2 Read the blog and match the photos (A–C) with paragraphs 2, 3 and 4.

A Paragraph ....   **B** Paragraph ....   **C** Paragraph ....

3 e Read the blog again and choose the correct answers.

1 How does the writer feel about the project?
  A happy that it's finished
  B surprised that it was interesting
  C worried about presenting it
  D bored by the topic

2 How is the Sky Garden different from a normal public garden?
  A it's bigger
  B it's more expensive to visit
  C it's got different plants
  D it's inside a building

3 What can't the writer understand about the second garden?
  A why it's often empty
  B why it was designed in this way
  C why it has this name
  D why it doesn't have many plants

4 What does the writer think about the last garden?
  A they should have left the gardens as they were
  B it was really lucky the gardens were found
  C the gardens would look even better if they spent more money
  D the gardens should be advertised more

5 What might the teacher, Miss Parker, say about the writer's presentation?
  A You've given really good, detailed descriptions of the design of each garden.
  B I like the way you've chosen three very different types of garden to present.
  C The background information about all the trees and plants is extremely well researched and interesting.
  D I particularly enjoy your focus on city gardens and the reasons for having them.

4 Match the idiomatic phrases in bold in the blog (1–6) with their meanings (A–F).

1 for a start   **A** looked after
2 in the open air   **B** outside
3 pretty amazing   **C** firstly
4 have no idea   **D** the final thing to do
5 last on my list   **E** very surprising
6 took care of   **F** do not know

5 Complete the sentences with the correct form of the phrases from Ex 4.

1 I usually .... my friend's dog while she is away.

2 We sometimes go to see concerts ....

3 I couldn't do the homework. .... , I couldn't remember at it was, and then I couldn't find my dictionary.

4 Nearly finished. .... is get flowers for mum.

5 The film was .... – I loved it!

6 I'm sorry, but I .... what we've got to do for homework.

So, what are the most interesting things I've learned this month? Our project for Miss Parker on public gardens sounded really boring, but it turned out to be amazing! We had to research several unusual gardens and then present them to the class – not something I usually enjoy! I chose the UK and started browsing. Here's my presentation.

"Some areas are wild, like a jungle, while others are formal and peaceful."

Unusual gardens in the UK

When we think about public gardens in a city, we usually think about big parks with trees and grass where people can sit and chat. Well, the Sky Garden in London is nothing like that. **For a start**, it isn't **in the open air**. It's on the top three floors of a skyscraper! The Sky Garden is the highest public garden in London, with wonderful views across the city. It cost a lot to build and has many beautiful, colourful plants. I think it looks **pretty amazing**!

The second garden I looked at is in Scotland, and it isn't in a city but in the countryside. It's called The Garden of Cosmic Speculation! I still **have no idea** what the reason is for calling it that, but it's linked to science and maths. The designer, Charles Jencks, creates gardens with mathematical shapes. Unlike other gardens there aren't many flowers but it's clever and unusual. Another strange thing about this garden is that it's only open to visitors for one day every year! This definitely makes the place special. And, for most of the time, very empty!

Last on my list is a garden in south-west England. This garden is very popular and has another wonderful name – The Lost Gardens of Heligan. They were created almost 200 years ago. Then no one **took care of** them and no one remembered that they were there. In 1990, someone saw a door in a wall which led into the gardens. What a surprise! People restored them and now they are beautiful again. Some areas are wild, like a jungle, while others are formal and peaceful. I love the two enormous plant sculptures: the Giant's Head and the Mud Maid. They look like people growing out of the ground!

Three amazing gardens, and one great project – thanks, Miss Parker!

6 The great outdoors

GRAMMAR

1 🔊 **6.1 Listen to a voicemail about visiting an animal safari park and answer the questions. Tick the animals the boy mentions.**

elephants ☐   monkeys ☐

lions ☐   birds ☐

2 🔊 **6.2 What did some animals do when he went there last month?**

A made the car dirty

B frightened the people in the car

C damaged something on the car

3 🔊 **6.3 Listen again and complete the advice the boy gives.**

1 You .... drive through the whole park.

2 There are a lot of rules about what you .... and .... do.

3 You .... feed the animals.

4 You .... keep your windows closed.

5 You .... drive through.

6 You .... take some photos.

4 Complete the sentences with the correct form of *can*, *must* or *have to*. Make positive and negative sentences.

1 When you visit us on Saturday, your mum .... park on our drive because Dad's car is in the garage, or she .... park opposite our house.

2 We .... finish this geography project until next Friday, so we've got lots of time.

3 You .... touch that dog – he can be dangerous if he doesn't know you.

4 We .... go through the park before 9.30 p.m. because it closes at night.

5 You .... bring some strong shoes because we're going hiking across the hills on Sunday!

6 I hate that moment when the teacher says: 'You .... turn over your exam papers now.' And then the moment when he says: 'You .... stop writing now.'

5 Choose the correct words to complete the sentences.

1 I took a photo of **me / myself** with my dog to send to my Spanish friend.

2 Birds often wash **them / themselves** in the water on the bird table.

3 Tim asked **me / myself** for some information about bears so I sent it to **him / himself**.

4 I showed my younger sister how to get onto the website and then she did it by **her / herself**.

5 It's not a good idea to walk home at night by **you / yourself**. Get a taxi.

6 There was a fox in our garden last night and mum left some food out for **him / himself**.

6 Choose the correct words and phrases to complete the blog.

Yesterday I found a website that gives advice about how we can help the wildlife in our gardens. Here are some of their tips and some dos and don'ts!

You [1]**can / can't** put out food, but you [2]**don't have to / mustn't** put out too much or the animals will start to rely on it and not hunt for [3]**them / themselves**.

You [4]**can't / mustn't** leave out junk food for [5]**them / themselves**, like white bread or biscuits, because this is sometimes dangerous for their health. The best thing is to mix up nuts and seeds [6]**you / yourself**, so that you know what's in it.

You [7]**don't have to / can't** put out food all year because some animals, like birds, don't eat much in certain months.

You [8]**don't have to / mustn't** put bird feeders too close to windows or the birds might fly into the glass. And you [9]**have to / can** try to put bird feeders where squirrels can't reach them! I think that is nearly impossible!

You [10]**can / can't** leave food out for hedgehogs, but you [11]**don't have to / mustn't** give them milk, because it's bad for them.

Finally, you [12]**must / can** try to leave some old leaves or bits of wood around in the garden so that small animals, like insects, can find cover and be safe. Happy wildlife watching!

7 Write sentences that are true about your local park or area in the countryside.

1 We have to ....

....

2 We mustn't ....

....

3 We can ....

....

4 We don't have to ....

....

VOCABULARY

1 Name the animals in the pictures.

1	6 ....
2	7 ....
3	8 ....
4	9 ....
5	10 ....

2 Complete the sentences with the correct words.

blind   clever   colourful   friendly   powerful   sharp

1 Many baby animals are .... when they are born. They only start to see later.

2 Wolves have fur all over their bodies and very .... teeth.

3 Frogs have .... legs and can jump very high.

4 My favourite insect is the butterfly because they have such pretty, ... wings.

5 Foxes are .... animals and can find ways to get food from difficult places.

6 Some animals look .... , but they aren't – they're dangerous!

3 🔊 6.4 Complete the conversation about choosing a picture for a project on sea animals. Use a verb from box 1 and a preposition from box 2. There is one gap that only needs a verb. Listen and check.

1

biting   climbing   diving   hunting
jumping   landing

2

for   into   on   out of   up

A: These photos of animals are all brilliant, but we have to choose just one for the project. It's hard! I like this one – where the seabirds are ¹........................... the water from high up in the sky to catch the fish. Their wings are so powerful. Or this one, where the bird is ²........................... a rock to dry its feathers.

B: Yeah – they're both cool. But my favourite is the dolphin which is ³........................... the water using its powerful tail to lift it into the air. The penguins are amazing too – in this picture they're ⁴........................... fish – sometimes they swim more than a hundred miles! And this picture where they are ⁵........................... the rocks and steep paths to feed their babies is great. They look so tired but happy.

A: Or what about this picture of the catfish – it's ⁶........................... a smaller fish that it has caught, and you can see all the sharp teeth!

Extend

4 Match the animals (1–8) and their definitions (A–H).

1 an insect that bites	**A**	zebra
2 a tall animal with a long neck	**B**	giraffe
3 a fish that can bite and sometimes kill people	**C**	donkey
4 an animal from Australia that travels by jumping	**D**	shark
5 a bird that can talk	**E**	mosquito
6 an animal, like a horse, with black and white stripes	**F**	elephant
7 a very big, heavy animal that is grey	**G**	parrot
8 a strong animal, like a horse, with long ears	**H**	kangaroo

5 🔊 6.5 Listen to the radio programme and complete the information about sharks with the correct words.

attack   dangerous   fight   grow   smooth   survive

Sharks can be very ¹........................... fish. They can bite and kill humans if they are swimming because they think they are sea animals that they hunt for food. These animals, like other fish, don't have fur or feathers, but they've got very ²........................... bodies, without the scales that fish normally have, to travel through the water easily.
When they are hungry they find big groups of fish and ³........................... them from underneath.
Some sharks can ⁴........................... in both salt and fresh water, and the biggest sharks can ⁵........................... up to 4.6 metres! They don't usually eat other sharks, but they sometimes ⁶........................... each other if they are kept in sea life centres.

51

LISTENING

1 🔊 6.6 **Listen to seven conversations. Tick the topics the people talk about.**

A seeing animals in the countryside ☐

B a birthday party ☐

C sunbathing ☐

D a visit to a zoo ☐

E packing for a holiday ☐

F news for drivers ☐

G a mobile phone ☐

H an exhibition ☐

I getting to a beach ☐

J moving house ☐

2 e 🔊 6.7 **Listen again and choose the correct answers.**

1 What can the girl see from her bedroom window?

2 What's the weather going to be like in England at the weekend?

3 How did the boy get to the beach?

4 What did the girl see yesterday?

5 How did the boy get the information he needed?

6 Which is the girl's newest phone app?

7 What is the girl going to pack?

it's, there is / there are

3 **Choose *it's* or *there's* to complete the rules.**

1 Used to describe what something is like: **it's / there's**

2 Used to say something exists: **it's / there's**

3 Used to talk about the weather: **it's / there's**

4 Used to make a general statement about an experience: **it's / there's**

4 **Match the examples (A–D) with the rules in Ex 3 (1–4).**

A It's quite cold at the moment. ....

B It's lovely to watch the wildlife in the garden. ....

C There's an interesting article on the website. ....

D I didn't understand the question. It was very confusing. ....

5 **Choose the correct words to complete the information.**

New Forest Walks

If you're looking for a short but beautiful walk, ¹**it's / there's** one that starts at Dibden Enclosure and finishes at Ipley Cross Road. ²**It's / There's** about two kilometres and ³**it's / there are** lots of very old trees to see on the way. ⁴**It's / There's** one tree which is hundreds of years old and very big. ⁵**It's / There's** about halfway along the walk. ⁶**It's / There's** very pretty with plenty of wild flowers at this time of year too, and beautiful views across the valley. If ⁷**it's / there's** a clear day, you can see across to the Isle of Wight.

SPEAKING

1 The Speaking Part 3 task is a conversation. Read the examiner's comments (1–6) and decide which student, Rosa or Katya, did better in the task.

> **1** Rosa interrupted her partner quite a lot.
>
> **2** Rosa talked for a long time before asking Katya her opinion.
>
> **3** Katya made several suggestions about why the people might want to take a book.
>
> **4** Katya disagreed with Rosa about the book, but she was polite.
>
> **5** Katya gave a short comment and then asked Rosa's opinion about the points.
>
> **6** Rosa disagreed with Katya on a few points, but she didn't give a reason.

.... did better.

2 Complete the phrases with the correct words from the box.

about   disagree   idea   more   with

1 I'm not sure .... that because …

2 I think camping is .... sensible because …

3 I think that's the best .... because …

4 Yes, I agree .... you.

5 No, I .... because …

3 🔊 6.8 Read the task below and look at the pictures. Listen to two students doing the task. Which picture do they <u>not</u> mention?

....

> Three friends are planning a day's walking in the hills. Here are some things they might need. Talk together about taking these different things, and decide which is the most important.

4 🔊 6.9 Complete the sentences from the conversation. Listen again to check.

1 OK, shall we start .... the map?

2 How .... the sandwiches? I think they're really important.

3 I disagree .... they're quite heavy to carry.

4 I'm not sure .... that. I'd like sandwiches.

5 But .... my opinion the strong boots are the most important thing to have when you go walking in the hills.

6 Yes, it's more sensible to have those .... a map or a torch.

7 I agree, the boots are the .... important thing.

8 They're definitely .... important than sandwiches!

5 Here are some more things the friends could take with them. Make notes about what you could say about them. Plan to use some of the phrases from Ex 2. Then record your ideas about each item.

1 a camera

....

2 a mobile phone

....

3 a bottle of water

....

4 sunglasses

....

6 Read the follow-up questions. Make notes and then record your answers.

1 Would you like to go on a day's walking tour in the hills? Why? / Why not?

....

....

2 What would you take with you on a long journey? Why?

....

....

What to take on a hiking trip

WRITING

an article

1 For each sentence, cross out the word that doesn't make sense.

1 A beach can be
clear   huge   peaceful

2 The sea can be
calm   bright   cool

3 A room can be
bright   clear   huge

4 The weather can be
cool   calm   huge

5 A conversation can be
loud   silent   calm

6 A swimming pool can be
silent   cool   clear

2 Match the sentences (1–8) with their follow-up sentences (A–H).

1 The river is very peaceful at night time. ....

2 The day is very bright. ....

3 The music is very loud. ....

4 The lake is huge. ....

5 The garden is lovely and cool. ....

6 The street is silent at night. ....

7 The view from the hill is clear today. ....

8 The sea is calm. ....

A There's a lot of sunshine.

B People are dancing.

C It's like a mirror.

D It's two kilometres round.

E You can see the town five miles away.

F There aren't any cars or lorries.

G There are just the noises from the wind in the trees and the moving water.

H There are trees that block the sun.

3 Complete the sentences with *feels, looks* or *sounds*.

1 The little house in the forest .... like a picture in a story.

2 The dry sand .... lovely under my feet.

3 The view from your room .... amazing. I must visit soon.

4 It .... very cool in here – it's good to get out of the sun.

5 The beach .... busy this morning. I can hear a lot of chatting and some music.

6 From the photos the campsite .... perfect. Let's go there!

4 Read the question and the article. Which would be the best title for the article?

A Calm and quiet

B A popular place

C Walks by the sea

You see this notice on an English language website.

> # Articles wanted!
> What's your favourite place in the countryside?
> Write an article telling us about your favourite place in the countryside. Why do you like it and how often do you go there?
> We'll put the best articles on the website.
> Write your article in about 100 words.

A magical place

Near my home there are some beautiful forests, and also a National Park with amazing mountains and two or three blue lakes. It's hard to choose my favourite place because there are a lot! But I really like going to the secret beach near my house. It's a lovely place with white sand and clear water. There aren't many tourists there, so it usually feels very peaceful and you can often see wild horses. Some people think they look dangerous but they're not! I spend a lot of time on the beach with my family. It's amazing. I know it sounds idyllic, but please don't tell anyone! I like it because it's quiet!

5 Read the article again and list the descriptive adjectives and descriptive verbs the writer uses.

1 Adjectives: ....
....

2 Verbs: ....

6 **e** Read the task again and write your own article. Remember:

1 make notes before you write

2 answer the questions

3 give your article an interesting title

4 use descriptive adjectives and verbs

5 divide your article into a couple of paragraphs

6 read it through and check your article when you're finished

UNIT CHECK

1 Complete the park rules with the correct form of *can*, *must* or *have to*. For some rules there may be more than one possible answer.

PARK RULES

1 You .... use this park during the week from 8.30 a.m. to 7.30 p.m.

2 At the weekend it closes later but you .... enter after 9.30 p.m.

3 Users of the park .... sit on the grass or the benches but .... walk through the bushes or flowerbeds.

4 You .... keep dogs on a lead.

5 You .... use the rubbish bins or take your litter away with you.

6 Entry to the park is free and also you .... pay for parking during the week.

2 Complete the dialogue with *it's | there's | there are.*

A: Hi! ¹............................ a group run this Saturday. Do you want to go?

B: Ah – ²............................ my brother's birthday on Saturday. I'm going to the beach with him. Where does the run take place?

A: Well, ³............................ in the afternoon at Green Park. ⁴............................ going to be about fifty runners. I love the group runs in the park. ⁵............................ fun to run with other people!

B: You're right. ⁶............................ better than running on your own. I can ask my brother. He might prefer it to the beach.

3 Complete the sentences with the correct words.

1 This painting is brilliant. Did you do it **you / yourself**?

2 My cat sees **it / itself** in the mirror and thinks it's another cat!

3 I told **you / yourself** about the documentary yesterday. Do you remember?

4 My friend was ill so I had to go for a walk by **me / myself**.

5 The teacher helped **us / ourselves** with the animal project.

4 Use the clues to complete the animal puzzle.

Across

3 It's a sea animal that likes jumping and playing.

6 It's a night animal and it's blind.

8 It's very small and lives in the countryside and sometimes in our houses.

9 It's usually green; it jumps and lives on land and in water.

11 It's a water bird and it spends a lot of time in the water.

12 It's an insect which flies and has colourful wings.

14 It's a big, wild and dangerous orange cat, with brown and black stripes.

Down

1 It's like a wild dog with sharp teeth.

2 It's a very tall animal.

4 It's a big animal with sharp teeth, and it lives in groups.

5 It's an insect and it bites people.

7 It's sometimes naughty and it climbs trees.

10 A bird that can sometimes learn to say words.

12 A black and yellow flying insect that visits flowers.

13 It's an animal which lives in towns and gardens. It's often red.

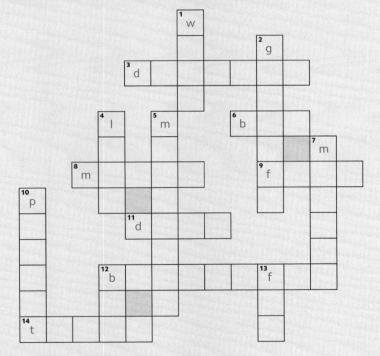

5 Complete the words in the sentences.

1 Lions have p_ _ _ _ _ _ _ legs and s_ _ _ _ teeth that b_ _ _ easily.

2 Some animals that live underground don't need to see: they're b_ _ _ _ _.

3 There was a bird fight in our garden and there were f_ _ _ _ _ _ _ on the grass.

4 Bears have brown or black f_ _ and h_ _ _ small animals for food.

5 Bees' w_ _ _ _ move very quickly to keep them in the air.

6 Some fish can d_ _ _ a long way under water and also j_ _ _ out into the air.

7 If a butterfly l_ _ _ _ on your hand, it's good luck!

REVIEW: UNITS 1–6

1 Choose the correct verb forms to complete what the people say about their plans for the weekend.

(1) I **'m going to spend / spend** most of the weekend revising because my exams **start / are going to start** next Monday!

(2) I **do / 'm doing** a fun football training day this Saturday. I **'m asking / 'm going to ask** some of my friends if they want to come too.

(3) On Saturday evening, I **'m having / have** some friends round to my house to watch a film together. I think my mum **orders / is going to order** some pizzas for us.

(4) My best friend from my old school **is coming / is going to come** to stay for the weekend. Her train **is going to arrive / arrives** at six o'clock on Friday and I can't wait!

2 Complete the blog with the correct verbs. There are two verbs you don't need.

do   get   give   have   make   move   settle   take   tell

outdoor learning

Everyone has their own style of learning. I've always found it hard to ¹........................... down and work hard at school. I just feel I need to ²........................... around and **do** things. That's why I'm so pleased that my school has introduced outdoor learning. We go out into the forest once a week and do all kinds of fun activities. It's great! The teachers don't ³........................... us off if we want to explore or ⁴........................... a go at climbing a tree. And if we want to build a shelter or make a fire, the teacher lets us ⁵........................... it a try. It's made a big difference to me. I feel more confident now. I don't ⁶........................... as many mistakes with my school work now, and I'm starting to ⁷........................... better grades, too!

3 Complete the posts with the verbs in brackets and *will* or *may / might*.

What's the future for space travel?
Tell us your predictions!

I'm sure people ¹........................... (travel) to Mars in the next ten years. They ²........................... (not stay) there and build homes there yet, though. That seems much less likely.

I think it's possible that people ³........................... (forget) about space travel over the next ten years. I'm certain there ⁴........................... (be) more serious problems for the world to think about, like climate change.

I really don't believe people ⁵........................... (find) a way to travel such long distances through space. They ⁶........................... (send) robot spaceships to other planets, though – that's possible.

4 Choose the correct words to complete the article.

WHO REALLY WANTS TO WEAR
DESIGNER CLOTHES?

Most people like to follow fashion in their clothes, and every year ¹**the newest / newer / new enough** fashion styles appear in the big fashion shows around the world. But would you really want to wear the clothes? The ²**as expensive / too expensive / most expensive** clothes seem to be designed to be completely impossible to wear! They don't look ³**more comfortable / as comfortable / less comfortable** as the jeans and T-shirts you can buy in any shopping mall, and they are definitely ⁴**more suitable / as suitable / less suitable** for normal life. For example, the sleeves might be ⁵**longest / long enough / too long**, so they would get in the way when you do everyday activities or even when you just wash your hands! That new fashion coat might look good but it won't be ⁶**warm enough / warmer / warmest** in cold weather. That's why I'm quite happy to buy 'normal' clothes that are much ⁷**less cheap / cheaper / cheap enough** than designer ones, and ⁸**better / not as good / too good** for real life!

5 Read the clues and write the words.

1 I'm not tall and I'm not short – just normal. I'm a_ _ _ _ _ _ h_ _ _ _ _.

2 I get these on my face in the summer. They're small and brown. I've got f_ _ _ _ _ _ _.

3 My hair isn't fair. It's very d_ _ _.

4 I wear these so that my teeth will look great in a few years. I wear b_ _ _ _ _.

5 I love rings and necklaces, and earrings too. I wear a lot of j_ _ _ _ _ _ _.

6 My hair isn't straight. It's c_ _ _ _.

6 Read the beach safety rules, then choose the correct words to complete the sentences.

1 Everyone **can / must** swim between the two red and yellow flags.

2 You **have to / mustn't** stay out of the water if the red flag is flying. You **must / can't** go swimming then because it's dangerous.

3 You **mustn't / don't have to** surf where other people are swimming. You **can't / must** stay in the surfing area.

4 You **mustn't / don't have to** wear sun cream, but it's a good idea to wear it.

Beach safety

- The area between the two red and yellow flags is safe for swimming for all ages. Swimming is allowed in other parts of the beach, but only for strong swimmers.

- Don't go in the water if the red flag is flying – the water is dangerous!

- Surfers – stay in the area with the black and white flags. Do not surf in the swimming area.

- There's no rule about using sun cream, but we recommend it very strongly.

7 Complete the animal profiles with the correct words.

bite   clever   climb   dive   friendly   fur   hunt   powerful

Amazing animals

Everyone knows that dolphins are very ¹.......................... animals – in fact, they are one of the most intelligent animals in the world. It's usually safe to be in the water with dolphins – they are very ².......................... and love spending time with humans. They are amazing swimmers and can ³.......................... down very quickly to catch small fish to eat. They can also swim fast, using their ⁴.......................... tails to push them through the water.

Wolves have very thick ⁵.......................... , which means they can stay warm even in very cold weather. Did you know they can also ⁶.......................... trees? Most people are scared of these beautiful animals, and it's true that they ⁷.......................... and kill other animals for food. They have sharp teeth, and they might ⁸.......................... you if they're scared. But if they are left alone in the wild, they aren't really dangerous to us.

8 **e** Write one word in each gap.

Just looking is boring!

Most people enjoy driving into the countryside to admire the view, or maybe walking through a forest to enjoy the peace. But for some people this just isn't exciting ¹.......................... . They hate the idea of just looking at the countryside, and not doing ².......................... else. They want to challenge ³.......................... to do something fast or dangerous. For them, being on a boat on a fast-flowing river is much ⁴.......................... fun than having a quiet picnic by a waterfall. ⁵.......................... wants to drive up a mountain, they might say, when you can climb up it or fly over it? ⁶.......................... are hundreds of extreme sports which you can do in the countryside, so if you get bored with just looking, maybe you should think about doing something more exciting!

Food for thought

READING

1 Complete the messages with the correct words.

chains   cost   hugs   pop-up   promotions   short   tasty

Suggestions for good food in
LONDON?

StefanB   Add message | Report

Hi, I'm in London for a few days and am looking for some places to eat that serve good food and don't ¹........................... a fortune. Any suggestions?

JollyJo   Add message | Report

I guess you want to avoid the big restaurant ²........................... because their food is the same all over the world! If you're ³........................... of money, some of the markets are a good place to find ⁴........................... food. Brick Lane is my favourite!

Mia_M   Add message | Report

Look out for ⁵........................... cafés in different parts of the city. They're usually there for about a week, and the food is often excellent. There's a list of them online.

Paul88   Add message | Report

A lot of restaurants in the Covent Garden area have special ⁶........................... at lunchtime, so you can often get a really good meal for a reasonable price.

StefanB   Add message | Report

Thanks for your help, everyone – big ⁷........................... to you all!

2 Complete the meanings with the correct form of words and expressions from Ex 1.

1 Food that is .... is very good to eat.
2 A .... shop or café is one that is only there for a short time.
3 If you give someone a .... , you hold them in your arms.
4 If something .... , it is very expensive.
5 A .... is a group of shops or restaurants that all have the same name.
6 A .... is a special low price for a short time.
7 If you are .... , you don't have enough.

3 Read the article about food on page 59. Why do you think the writer wrote the article?

A to encourage everyone to eat more healthy food
B to make people think about the importance of food for athletes
C to explain why top athletes need to eat particular foods

4 🄔 Read the article again. Choose the best sentence (A–H) for each gap. There are three extra sentences which you do not need to use.

A They travel 200 kilometres a day for three weeks, often over mountains.
B When you think about it, that's a lot of food!
C Footballers often run 10 kilometres during a game.
D But food is even more important for top athletes.
E Some athletes find it difficult to eat healthy food all the time.
F But food isn't only about energy.
G Fish is a really important food for athletes.
H Tennis champion Rafael Nadal has admitted that he enjoys eating chocolate.

5 Read the article again. Decide if the sentences are true (T) or false (F).

1 Not everyone is aware how important it is to eat healthy food. ....
2 Rafael Nadal doesn't worry about getting heavier. ....
3 The writer thinks it might not be fun if you have to eat a lot of food every day. ....
4 Cyclists in the Tour de France have big meals all through the day. ....
5 Maria Jimenez only cooks special food for the cyclists when they do well. ....

6 Complete the meanings with the bold words and expressions in the text.

1 Your............................ is how you are feeling.
2 If you .... , your body becomes heavier.
3 .... are the amount of energy that food contains.
4 Your .... is all the food that you eat.
5 .... is something that gives power to a machine or a person.
6 When you .... food, you eat it.

7 Complete the sentences with the correct form of the words from Ex 6.

1 Sam is in a bad .... today because he didn't win his race.
2 Your body needs .... in the same way as a car does.
3 Fruit and vegetables are an important part of a healthy ....
4 If you eat a lot of crisps and chocolate and don't do any exercise, you will ....
5 Most men need around 2,500 .... a day. Women and children need less.
6 It is important to .... enough food to give you the energy you need.

Food for winning

We all know that having a good **diet** and eating the right food is important. It helps our body to work well and keeps us fit and healthy. **1**........ This is because they work their bodies hard, almost to the limit of what is possible, and food is the **fuel** they need to keep going.

Some people might think it's a dream life. You're active every day, so you can eat as much as you want, and some stars do. **2**........ He can do this because he knows he won't **put on weight**. He trains every day, so his body uses all the energy he **takes in** through his food. Sounds good?

But what's it like when you *need* to eat a huge amount of food every day? Don't you think it might get just a little boring? Players in the football World Cup need to eat around 5,000 **calories** every day – that's twice as much as a normal person. **3**........ Imagine eating all your normal meals twice in the same day – and then doing the same the next day and the next.

Getting enough food is even more challenging for cyclists in the big races like the Tour de France. **4**........ To do this, they need to eat around 8,000 calories a day, most of it in the morning and evening. That's a lot of rice and pasta!

5........ Maria Jimenez is a chef for a top cycling team, and she believes that food is also very important for the cyclists' **mood**. She follows the race in her mobile kitchen and works hard to provide food that is healthy *and* enjoyable. 'The cyclists need energy, of course, but food also helps them to feel positive,' she says. 'If they do badly, they need something tasty to help them feel better, and if they do well, I make sure they get a nice dessert!'

7 Food for thought

GRAMMAR

relative clauses with *who* and *which*

1 🔊 7.1 Complete the quiz questions with *who* or *which*. Then do the quiz. Listen and check your answers.

FOOD QUIZ

1 You can eat pizza all over the world, but one country has a law .... says what ingredients restaurants are allowed to put on some of their pizzas. Which country is it?
A the USA   B Italy   C the UK

2 The ancient Greeks were people .... enjoyed their food! What did they mix with snow to make a kind of ice cream?
A sugar and lemons   B chocolate   C honey and fruit

3 What name is sometimes given to someone .... is rich or has a lot of power?
A a big cheese   B a big egg   C a big apple

4 There is one popular food .... dogs can't eat because it makes them ill. What is it?
A chocolate   B bread   C cake

5 The people .... first made the tomato sauce we now love to eat with burgers didn't sell it as a sauce. What did they sell it as?
A jam   B medicine   C soup

6 There is one popular meal .... American astronauts took with them into space when they travelled to the Moon on Apollo 11. What was it?
A burgers   B pizzas   C hotdogs

7 What is the country in the world .... produces the most coffee?
A Brazil   B Mexico   C India

8 Americans .... love pasta celebrate National Pasta Month once a year by eating a lot of their favourite food. Which month is it?
A August   B October   C December

2 Complete the joined sentences using a relative clause with *who* or *which*.

1 Sam's Place is a restaurant. It serves amazing burgers!
Sam's Place is .... amazing burgers!

2 A fruitarian is a person. He or she only eats fruit and nuts.
A fruitarian is .... fruit and nuts.

3 The restaurant has a new chef. She loves trying new dishes.
The restaurant has a new .... new dishes.

4 Sushi is a food. I have never eaten it.
Sushi is .... eaten.

5 Serving in a restaurant is a job. A lot of students do it.
Serving in a restaurant is .... do.

6 The chef is Spanish. She works at the restaurant on Broad Street.
The chef .... on Broad Street is Spanish.

3 Read the review of a restaurant. Then use information in the review to complete the sentences using relative clauses with *who* or *which*.

⭐☆☆☆☆   **Anna's Bistro – not good!**

We went to Anna's Bistro for lunch on Saturday and it was awful! The menu looked good, but then we noticed that a lot of things were only available in the evening. The waiter was polite when he served us, but he wasn't very helpful. We saw some of the kitchen staff and they didn't look very happy either. We ordered some dishes, and we were all really disappointed with them! One of my friends had fish. He was really ill afterwards, so I don't think it was very fresh!

I definitely won't go there again!

1 There were a lot of things on the menu .... at lunchtime.

2 The waiter .... but not very helpful.

3 The kitchen staff .... unhappy.

4 The dishes .... very disappointing.

5 The fish .... very fresh.

VOCABULARY

talking about food

1 Choose the correct words in the cooking advice.

How to cook the
PERFECT
apple cake

Leave the cake in the oven for 45 minutes to make sure it is **¹cooked / burned** right through to the middle and the apple is **²raw / soft**.

Be careful with the oven temperature. If the oven is too hot, the outside of the cake will be **³sour / burned** and the inside will still be **⁴hard / raw**.

Add plenty of apple, so you get a lot of **⁵salty / juicy** fruit in every bite.

Don't forget to add sugar to make sure it is lovely and **⁶sweet / dry**.

Enjoy!

2 Complete the words in the customer complaints.

1 These chips aren't cooked properly. Chips should be light brown and c_ _s_y!

2 These boiled carrots are too h_ _d. They should be nice and soft.

3 This bread is old. It's really d_y! And I can't eat the soup – it's too s_l_y.

4 There isn't enough sugar in this lemonade. It's too s_ _r.

5 There's so much chilli in this dish, it's too s_i_y for me.

3 Complete each sentence with the correct opposite of the adjective in bold.

juicy   raw   salty   soft   sour

1 Meat should always be .... and not **dry**.
2 Do you prefer **sweet** foods like chocolate or .... foods like crisps?
3 Some kinds of tofu are quite **hard**, but others are very ....
4 Oranges are **sweet**, but lemons are ....
5 You can eat peppers either .... or **cooked**.

4 🔊 7.2 Complete what these people say about their favourite recipes. There is one adjective in each group that you don't need. Then listen and check.

1 'I like making pizzas. I usually cook them in a hot oven, so the bottom of the pizza is lovely and .... .Then, on top, I put lots of .... tomatoes, and some cheese, which gives that lovely .... taste.'

salty   burned   juicy   crispy

2 'We often go to a Vietnamese restaurant in town that has amazing noodles. They are .... and full of flavour. You can ask them to make them .... if you like hot food, but I don't! I tried making them at home once but I did something wrong because they were black and .... on the bottom!'

raw   soft   burned   spicy

3 'My mum makes this amazing chocolate dessert. It's like a small cake. There's lots of sugar and chocolate in it, so it's really .... , then she only puts it in the oven for a short time, so it's .... and quite hard on the outside but still lovely and .... on the inside – mmm!'

cooked   soft   spicy   sweet

4 'My friend Hana makes amazing sushi. You have to cook the rice, of course, but all the other ingredients are .... It's made with fish and rice, and lots of Japanese pepper so it's quite .... It's really good for you, and it's easy to make because it can't go wrong – you don't cook the fish, so it can never be .... !'

raw   spicy   burned   sour

Extend

5 Complete the sentences with the correct words.

baked   bitter   frozen   grilled   roast   sticky

1 I always keep some .... vegetables in my freezer because they're quick and easy to cook.
2 Dark chocolate has quite a .... taste, so you need to add sugar when you use it in cooking.
3 There's a nice café near where I work, so I sometimes go there and have a .... potato for lunch.
4 I often do a .... chicken for dinner because it's so easy – you just put the chicken in the oven and cook it for about an hour!
5 I love .... fish, especially if it's done on a barbecue.
6 Baklava is a .... Greek dessert made with honey and nuts.

LISTENING

1 🔊 **7.3 Listen and match the five conversations (1–5) with the correct topics (A–E).**

A explaining how to prepare food ....

B an excellent programme ....

C advice about food for sport ....

D planning a meal with friends ....

E a disappointing meal ....

2 e 🔊 **7.4 Listen again and choose the correct answer for each question.**

1 You will hear two friends talking about a takeaway meal.

Why is the boy not happy?

A There was a mistake with his order.

B The pizza isn't very good quality.

C The food isn't warm enough.

2 You will hear a girl telling her friend about a new TV show.

What does she say about the show?

A It's good because the chefs show their emotions.

B Unlike many cookery shows, it isn't a competition.

C The chefs cook traditional dishes from around the world.

3 You will hear a girl showing a friend how to make a cake.

She says the most important thing is

A to work quickly.

B to have the oven at exactly the right temperature.

C to use the correct quantities of ingredients.

4 You will hear two friends planning a barbecue.

They agree that

A they should ask their guests to bring drinks with them.

B they will make some desserts.

C they don't need to cook any vegetarian food.

5 You will hear a girl talking to her sports coach.

The coach advises the girl

A to eat a big breakfast on the day of the match.

B to have a big meal the night before.

C to have a snack just before the match.

3 **Read the sentences from the audio. Match the bold words with the meanings.**

1 I agree. Cold pizza's **horrible**!

2 This is the list of **ingredients**.

3 They **share** their cooking traditions with each other.

4 It's a really easy recipe to **follow**.

5 My mum bought us some burgers, and some **stuff** for salad.

6 Don't **fill yourself up** on breakfast.

A do what a person or thing suggests

B things

C not nice to eat

D eat a lot, so you feel full

E give information to other people

F the different kinds of food that you need to make a dish

adverbs

4 **Complete the comments with adverbs formed from the adjectives in brackets.**

What food habits annoy you?
Our readers tell us what makes them angry.

Emily, 15

I try to eat ¹.......................... (healthy), and most of the time I do quite ².......................... (good). So it really annoys me when other people buy chocolates or cakes and then offer them to me – it's impossible to say no!

Stan, 16

The thing I really hate is when people eat ³.......................... (noisy) in the cinema. If you have to eat while you're watching a film, just do it ⁴.......................... (quiet)!

Tabby, 16

I hate it when I've cooked a meal for people and then they eat it really ⁵.......................... (fast). I've made a big effort by cooking the food. I think they should eat it more ⁶.......................... (slow) so they can enjoy it!

Josh, 15

I try ⁷.......................... (hard) not to look at my phone while I'm eating with other people because I think it's rude, and I think other people should do the same. So if friends reach for their phone during meals, I ask them ⁸.......................... (polite) to put it away.

SPEAKING

1 Match the sentence halves to make sentences for describing things in a photo.

1 It looks ....
2 It's a type ....
3 I'm not ....
4 I can't ....
5 It's something you ....

A of large pan for cooking fish.
B remember the word in English.
C like a very big spoon with holes in it.
D use for making cakes.
E sure of the word in English.

2 🔊 **7.5 Look at the photo and complete the description. Listen and check.**

The photo shows two women. The woman on the left is eating something. It **¹**........ a cookie which they've made. The other woman is going to take one too. In front of them there is something white. I'm **²**........ of the word in English, but it's something you **³**........ making cookies. They're both wearing something over their clothes. I **⁴**........ the word in English, but it's a **⁵**........ cover for your clothes, to keep them clean when you're cooking.

1 A looks like	**B** seems	**C** might have
2 A don't know	**B** can't see	**C** not sure
3 A need to	**B** use for	**C** have in
4 A don't say	**B** didn't know	**C** can't remember
5 A type of	**B** kind	**C** like a

3 Choose the correct words to complete the sentences from a café.

1 I'd **like / have / want** a black coffee, please.
2 OK. **I come / I'll be / I am** right back.
3 Are you **ready / agreed / decided** to order?
4 What **are / can / would** you like to drink?
5 I'll **have / order / like** a burger and fries, please.
6 And **with / for / to** you?

4 Look at the sentences in Ex 3 again and decide who says them. Write W (waiter) or C (customer).

1 ....   3 ....   5 ....
2 ....   4 ....   6 ....

5 Choose the best response.

1 Are you ready to order?
   A I'll be right back.
   B Yes, please.
2 I'd like a coffee, please.
   A Large or small?
   B What would you like to drink?
3 And for you?
   A What would you like?
   B I'd like an orange juice, please.
4 Two coffees, please.
   A OK, I'll be right back.
   B Just a small one, please.

6 🔊 **7.6 Complete the conversation with what the waitress says. Listen and check.**

And for you?   Are you ready to order?
Large or small?   OK, I'll be right back.
What would you like to drink?

Waitress:	Hello. **¹**...
Lena:	Yes, please. I'd like a burger with chips.
Waitress:	**²**...
Amina:	I'll have the same, please.
Waitress:	**³**...
Lena:	I'll have a milkshake, please.
Waitress:	**⁴**...
Lena:	Just a small one, please.
Amina:	And I'll have a diet cola, please.
Waitress:	**⁵**...

63

WRITING

an email

1 Read the email task and decide if the sentences are true (T) or false (F).

> Read this email from your English-speaking friend Ali, and the notes you have made. Write your email to Ali, using all the notes.

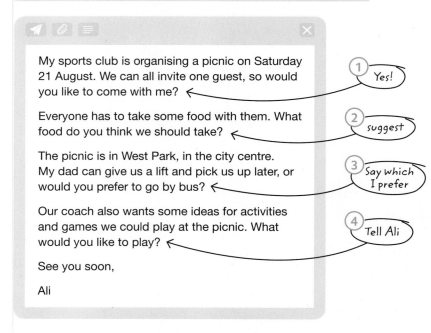

My sports club is organising a picnic on Saturday 21 August. We can all invite one guest, so would you like to come with me? ← ① Yes!

Everyone has to take some food with them. What food do you think we should take? ← ② suggest

The picnic is in West Park, in the city centre. My dad can give us a lift and pick us up later, or would you prefer to go by bus? ← ③ Say which I prefer

Our coach also wants some ideas for activities and games we could play at the picnic. What would you like to play? ← ④ Tell Ali

See you soon,

Ali

1 You should write an email to the sports club. ....
2 Ali is writing to invite you to an event. ....
3 In your email, you should include the four points in the notes. ....
4 Your email should be informal. ....

2 Look at the four notes in the email task. Choose how you should respond to each note.

1 A accept the invitation
  B explain why you want to come
2 A give information on some of your favourite food
  B suggest some food for the picnic
3 A explain what transport is like in the city
  B say how you would like to get to the picnic
4 A explain what games you would like to play
  B tell Ali what sports you usually do

3 Match the sentence halves.

1 Most people   **A** go by bus?
2 I'd love   **B** badminton is a good idea
3 I think   **C** to come to the picnic.
4 Shall we   **D** enjoy fresh fruit.

4 Complete the sentences with the correct words. Which four sentences could you use to answer the notes in the email task in Ex 1?

about	afraid	course	don't
how	more	say	sorry

1 I'm .... than happy to help with the picnic.
2 I'm .... , but I'll be away that weekend.
3 Of .... I can help you prepare some food.
4 Why .... we take some sandwiches and crisps?
5 What .... getting the bus?
6 I'd .... football is a good choice, because it's really exciting.
7 I'm .... I can't come to the picnic on Saturday.
8 .... about some small pizzas? Everyone loves pizza!

5 Choose two suitable beginnings and two suitable endings for the email task in Ex 1.

1 A Hi,
  B Dear Ali,
  C Hi Ali,
  D Dear Sir,
2 A Bye for now,
  B With best wishes,
  C Yours sincerely,
  D Cheers,

6 Look at the task in Ex 1 again and plan your email. Use the plan below.

Email beginning	
Note 1	
Note 2	
Note 3	
Note 4	
Email ending	

7 e Use your notes and write your email. Write about 100 words.

UNIT CHECK

1 Complete the crossword.

```
    ¹S │   │   │ ²C │   │   │
                  │   │
              ³r  │   │
              │   │
      ⁴S │   │   │   │   │
              │   │
      ⁵b │   │   │   │
```

Across

1 You add chilli and pepper if you want food to be this.
4 You add sugar if you want food to be this.
5 Your food is this if you cook it for too long and it goes black.

Down

2 This describes food you have made hot, for example in an oven.
3 This describes food you haven't cooked.
4 Lemons have this taste.

2 Complete what three people say about food, using the correct adjectives. There is one adjective in each group that you don't need.

① I like potatoes cooked in oil until they are brown and .... on the outside, but still .... on the inside.

crispy   salty   soft

② I love meat that isn't cooked for too long, so it's nice and ....
I hate it when it's cooked for too long and it goes ....

dry   juicy   raw

③ I don't like sweet snacks. I prefer .... snacks like crisps, but I don't like nuts because they are too .... to bite through.

hard   salty   sour

3 Complete the words in the restaurant review.

The Old Bakehouse   4.5 ◉◉◉◉◑

I had an amazing meal here for my birthday last week. I had the ¹r_ _ _t chicken, and it was lovely! One of my friends had some ²g_ _ _l_d lamb, and he said it was the best he'd ever had. My only complaint is that some of the vegetables were ³f_ _z_n, rather than fresh. The desserts were excellent too. I had a ⁴b_k_d pear with honey and spices, served with ice cream – lovely! The ⁵s_ _c_y chocolate cake also looked amazing, although one of my friends said the chocolate sauce to go with it was slightly ⁶b_ _t_r and not quite sweet enough. But it was a great meal, at a great price!

4 Complete the sentences (1–5) using *who* or *which* and the ideas (A–E).

1 A waiter is someone ....
2 Coffee is a drink ....
3 A guest is someone ....
4 A barbecue is a meal ....
5 A chef is someone ....

A you eat outside in the summer.
B cooks food in a restaurant.
C you invite to your house for a meal.
D a lot of people have in the morning.
E serves food in a restaurant.

5 Complete the article with an adverb made from the adjective in brackets.

What's new in food this year?

**Every year, supermarkets and restaurants try very ¹...........................
(hard) to find new ideas for food. They are always looking for ways to prepare food ²........................... (different), to give new, exciting flavours. This year look out for:**

Hawaiian food. It's made with lots of fish and ³...........................
(fresh) prepared vegetables. You can make a lot of the dishes quite ⁴........................... (cheap), and they're definitely good to eat.

Food that's good for your stomach. We're all trying to eat more ⁵........................... (healthy) now, so look out for foods that help your stomach to work ⁶........................... (good), to get you feeling healthy and full of energy!

Heme. A lot of people are trying to avoid meat ⁷...........................
(complete) and this could be the new 'fake' meat they are all waiting for. So vegetarians will soon be able to eat burgers quite ⁸........................... (happy), knowing that the meat doesn't come from an animal!

READING

1 Complete the text message with the correct words.

> challenging choice daily develop experts stage

Theatre course is fun. Lots of **1**............................ of things to do. No time to be bored! The **2**............................ give us great advice! We get **3**............................ private feedback sessions on how we're doing. Was quite **4**............................ to start with, but now I enjoy going up on the **5**............................ ! Great to **6**............................ new skills. Will call later. x

2 Read the adverts on page 67 for clubs and activities at a beach holiday hotel. Answer the questions.

Which activities

1 are at a specific time? ....

2 have an age restriction? ....

3 cost money? ....

3 e Read the task on the right. For each question choose the correct answer.

1 Ben ....   **3** Shona ....   **5** Jenny ....

2 Amy ....   **4** Max ....

4 Complete the collocations in the sentences with the correct verbs.

> come (x2) join perform spend take

1 We don't have set times, so just .... *along* any time.

2 If you .... *a club* you can make new friends.

3 My sister will .... *a song* at the concert on Friday.

4 Sometimes I .... *an afternoon* playing guitar and singing with my friends.

5 I'm going to .... *some waterskiing lessons* while I'm on holiday.

6 Please .... *on the trip* with us tomorrow – you'll enjoy it.

The young people below are all on a beach holiday and are looking for an activity to do. There are some adverts for activities they can do. Decide which activity would be most suitable for them.

1 Ben

Ben likes to be on the beach but gets bored sunbathing, and he can't swim. He's a talented artist and he'd like to do something interesting but not at the same time every day.

2 Amy

Amy is a confident sailor and her parents have offered to pay for her to learn a new watersport. She'd like to find out about the creatures that live in the sea.

3 Shona

Shona is very sociable but is looking for some time on her own. She likes sunbathing next to the sea with her friends, but after a while she'd like to get out of the sun and away from too much noise.

4 Max

Max is twelve. He's with his parents and wants to meet other young people. He's interested in nature and history. He'd like a morning activity as his family go into town after lunch.

5 Jenny

Jenny is fourteen and she wants something to do at the hotel in the evenings when she gets back from the beach. She plays the guitar.

There's a choice of great activities and clubs to join during your holiday. Here are just a few of the things you can do while mum and dad are sunbathing!

A Cool off!

Bored with the beach? Spend an afternoon inside the hotel at our 'chill out chamber'! You can have a massage to relax all those muscles you've been using swimming. Or, if you only want to relax around the indoor pool listening to gentle guitar music, come on in! Quiet time here – no chat, no cost. We're open every afternoon 2–5.

B Get busy

Are you artistic? Sandcastles aren't only for young children! Learn how to create wonderful statues and buildings on the beach with just sand and water. Our instructors are all very skillful and will teach you all need to know for free. The results don't last forever but your photos of them will amaze your friends. Who knows – you might win the Friday competition! You don't have to book – just come along any time.

C Take a ride

Don't stay on the beach or at the hotel for your whole holiday! Come on our trip to the Rockwood Theme Park. Only £25 for a whole day's fun for all the family. It's every Thursday and the coach leaves at 7.30. Enjoy the rides and the Sea Life exhibition.

D That's interesting!

Do you like learning? Then come on our fossil-hunting walks along the beach. The rocks and cliffs here are very old and they're famous for fossils (stones and rocks with the bones or shapes of very old animals and plants). Make new friends while you walk and search! We start every day at 8.30 at the hotel and return before 12.30.

E Time to socialise

Don't want to spend all your holiday with the parents? Why not join the hotel youth club and meet other people of your age in the evening? We organise beach barbecues, visits to hear local music and there's a club room to chat and play table tennis or computer games. It doesn't cost anything to join but you have to be thirteen to come along.

F Are you a winner?

Do you like singing or drama? Every week at the hotel we put on a show in the main dining room. We need YOU to perform a song or a dance or some comedy! We're looking for all ages and the best performance will get free waterskiing lessons for a week! Practice every day after dinner.

G Come on in!

The sea has many secrets. Take some diving lessons with us and find out about some of them. We offer lessons for complete beginners and also people who have done some diving before. Go deep under the water with our instructors and see the incredible plant and fish life. Ask at reception for prices and times.

H Get physical

The water-sports club is fantastic for anyone who wants some physical activity while staying at the hotel. Swimming in the sea is great but why don't you try waterskiing or windsurfing? Too scary? Then take some cheap sailing lessons – we have boats for one, two or three people – so get your mum or dad to come with you.

GRAMMAR

present perfect

1 Complete the grammar rules with the correct words.

| already   ever   just   never   past   when   yet (x2) |

1 We use the present perfect simple to talk about an experience in the recent ....

2 We don't say .... it happened.

3 We use .... to ask if something has happened.

4 We use .... to say that something has not happened.

5 We use .... when the experience happened a short time ago.

6 We use .... when something happened sooner than expected.

7 We use .... to say that something hasn't happened but we expect it to.

8 We use .... in questions to ask if something has happened recently.

2 🔊 8.1 **Listen to the phone conversation and decide which things are true. Tick the true statements.**

The girl has …

A seen the beach. ☐
B been to Malta before. ☐
C unpacked her bags. ☐
D gone round the hotel. ☐
E found the indoor pool. ☐
F put on sun cream. ☐

3 🔊 8.2 **Complete the sentences from the conversation. Listen again to check.**

1 .... to the beach yet?
2 I .... water so blue!
3 I .... to some beaches in Spain, Italy and France.
4 I .... unpacked.
5 I .... round the hotel yet.
6 I .... some on.

4 Complete the sentences using the present perfect simple.

1 parents / ever / travel in Africa?

....

2 Tom / just / walk into the café. I'll ask him to call you.

....

3 My brother and I / not be / to many other countries.

....

4 you / be / in the sea / already? That was quick!

....

5 Complete the email with one word (or a contraction) in each gap.

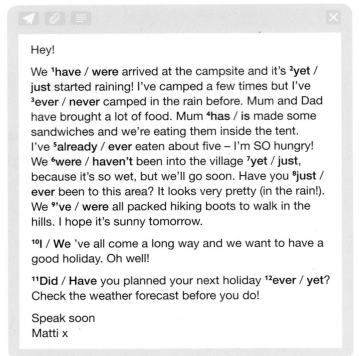

Hey!

We ¹**have / were** arrived at the campsite and it's ²**yet / just** started raining! I've camped a few times but I've ³**ever / never** camped in the rain before. Mum and Dad have brought a lot of food. Mum ⁴**has / is** made some sandwiches and we're eating them inside the tent. I've ⁵**already / ever** eaten about five – I'm SO hungry! We ⁶**were / haven't** been into the village ⁷**yet / just**, because it's so wet, but we'll go soon. Have you ⁸**just / ever** been to this area? It looks very pretty (in the rain!). We ⁹**'ve / were** all packed hiking boots to walk in the hills. I hope it's sunny tomorrow.

¹⁰**I / We** 've all come a long way and we want to have a good holiday. Oh well!

¹¹**Did / Have** you planned your next holiday ¹²**ever / yet**? Check the weather forecast before you do!

Speak soon
Matti x

6 Complete the reply email with the correct words.

Hi Matti!

Oh dear! I hope the rain ¹............................ stopped now! I've ²............................ been camping – I guess it can be quite uncomfortable? No, we haven't planned our next holiday ³............................ , but I've ⁴............................ been on a 'Holidays in Portugal' website. Some beach hotels ⁵............................ reduced their prices for next week. I'm going to tell mum and dad and perhaps we can go. I'd like some sun! Have you ⁶............................ been to Portugal? It looks brilliant.

See you soon

Jilly

VOCABULARY

travel and transport

1 Complete the words from the meanings.

1 You wait here for a train: p_ _ _ _ _ _ _
2 This is a person who is visiting another country on holiday: t_ _ _ _ _ _
3 This is a ticket to go somewhere and come back: r_ _ _ _ _
4 You sometimes need this to travel to another country: v_ _ _
5 You book this to stay in when you're on holiday: a_ _ _ _ _ _ _ _ _ _ _
6 This is the place in a hotel where you ask for help: r_ _ _ _ _ _ _ _
7 You need to take off your shoes and belt when you go through this: s_ _ _ _ _ _ _
8 This is the cost of a journey in a plane or train: f_ _ _
9 This is a person who is travelling in transport: p_ _ _ _ _ _ _ _
10 Here they check your case for things that aren't allowed into a country: c_ _ _ _ _ _

2 Complete the sentences with the correct words.

reservation	customs	guests	ID	platform	tourists

1 There are a lot of .... visiting the city this weekend.
2 You need to show your photo .... at the airport.
3 Dad made a .... at the restaurant for 8.30.
4 Only hotel .... can use the pool.
5 I think we're on the right .... for our train.
6 The .... official stopped us at the airport to check our bags.

3 Match the sentence halves.

1 I didn't pay ....
2 We went on a ....
3 My friends and I caught ....
4 I think we need to make ....
5 You go to that office over there to buy ....
6 Have your passports ready because you have to show some ....

A a train to a theme park just outside Paris.
B ID before getting on the plane.
C a reservation for the restaurant this evening.
D full fare until the age of 12.
E tickets for the performance.
F really long journey through the mountains.

4 🔊 8.3 **Listen to some people making comments about holidays and complete the sentences.**

1 I was looking forward to the .... of my friend from Italy but there was a .... and I had to wait two hours.
2 We took four cases to the USA but all our .... got lost so we had to buy new clothes.
3 You need .... when you go on holiday because you might be in an accident.
4 We went .... a day trip and we had a .... on the coach to tell us about the different places along the ....
5 We .... the bus into the town because there was a mistake on the .... , so we .... a taxi. Luckily we .... the bus back!
6 My dad's .... a lot by car but he's still bad at following ....

5 Complete Maddie's travel blog with the correct words.

caught	delay	directions	guide	had
insurance	on	route	take	travel

Our holiday in France

by Maddie

While we were in France we went **1**........................... a trip to Mont St Michel, a medieval town on an island. We wanted to **2**........................... by car and used my dad's phone to get **3**........................... . The **4**........................... to the place was quite complicated but our first view of the island was incredible. We drove the car over the bridge and parked, then **5**........................... a small bus to go up to the top of the Mount. We paid for a **6**........................... to take us round the beautiful cathedral. There are a lot of steps in the cathedral and my mum fell down some! She hurt her foot and we had to **7**........................... a taxi back to the car park because mum couldn't get on the bus. Of course, there was a **8**........................... getting back to the hotel. Luckily, we **9**........................... a reservation for dinner so Mum didn't have to walk far! We were all hungry! Mum had to go to a doctor the next day, but we had travel **10**........................... so it didn't cost anything.

8 Getting away

LISTENING

1 🔊 **8.4 Listen to a school radio interview with Mason, who has just been on a school skiing trip. Answer the questions.**

1 Why did Mason not go to Italy?
....

2 Which country did he go to on a skiing trip?
....

3 When did he have an accident?
....

4 Where did the students stay during the trip?
....

5 What was the name of the friend Mason made? ....

6 Where does his friend go to school?
....

2 e 🔊 **8.5 Listen again and choose the correct answers.**

1 Mason went on the skiing trip because
   A he likes going to other countries.
   B he passed all his exams.
   C he wanted to do a new sport.

2 While Mason was in the beginner's group he was
   A unhappy because he wasn't with his friends.
   B surprised that he made fast progress.
   C keen to get into a higher group.

3 Why did Mason have an accident?
   A He was hit by another student.
   B He went down a hill that was too advanced for him.
   C He found it impossible to control his speed.

4 What did Mason do instead of skiing?
   A He taught some waiters English.
   B He learned about Swiss culture.
   C He watched television.

5 What does Mason regret about the trip?
   A He didn't take a lot of photographs.
   B He didn't go to other parts of the country.
   C He didn't see his classmates very much.

6 What plan has Mason made to see his new Swiss friend, Marcel?
   A Marcel is coming to stay with Mason in London.
   B Mason is going to visit when Marcel starts studying.
   C Mason and Marcel are going to work together in the summer.

present perfect with *for* and *since*

3 Complete the time phrases with *for* or *since*.

1 .... three years
2 .... two months
3 .... my birthday
4 .... half an hour
5 .... 10th May
6 .... the beginning of March
7 2017
8 .... a few days
9 .... last Monday

4 Choose 5 of the time phrases in Ex 3 and write sentences that are true for you.

1 ....
2 ....
3 ....
4 ....
5 ....

5 🔊 **8.6 Listen to a phone conversation between two school friends talking about the girl's school trip. What is true about the school trip?**

A They're staying in Venice for the week.
B They're visiting different places in Italy.
C They're spending some time on the beach.

6 🔊 **8.7 Listen again and complete the sentences from the conversation using the verbs in brackets in the present perfect and *for* or *since*.**

1 We .... (be) here .... a week now and I love it!

2 We've seen lots of amazing things .... we arrived in Italy!

3 It .... (be) over 30 degrees .... 10 o'clock this morning.

4 I .... (visit) Venice and I remember the heat.

5 She .... (have) flu .... a few days and she .... (not / be) out of the hotel room .... yesterday morning.

6 One of my friends .... (be) ill with flu too .... a week.

7 I .... (have) a headache .... a couple of hours, but I think that's the sun – and the crowds.

8 I .... (not / see) so many people .... I was in London last summer.

SPEAKING

1 Complete the sentences for reaching agreement with the correct words.

both   choice   decide   guess   let's   shall   talked
with (x2)   would

1 I'm happy .... that.

2 I .... we just have different opinions.

3 Shall we .... on the best one?

4 We've .... about all the presents now.

5 I agree .... you about that.

6 .... choose this one.

7 We .... think this is a good idea.

8 My .... would be the ornament.

9 .... we choose the book?

10 I .... choose the painting.

2 🔊 8.8 Read the task below, then listen to Vera and Tomas discussing the presents. Who first mentions the different presents (1–6), Vera (V) or Tomas (T)?

1 book of photographs ....
2 box of biscuits ....
3 coffee cups ....
4 T-shirt ....
5 key ring ....
6 recipe book ....

3 🔊 8.9 Which present do Vera and Tomas choose? Listen again to check.

....

A student is on a school trip to a city in another country. Here are some ideas for a present to take home for her parents. Talk together about the different presents, and say which would be the best.

4 Below are more student answers from different conversations. Complete the answers with the correct words.

for   instance   opinion   think

1 I .... that it's a small painting of a bridge in Venice. My sister brought it back from a school trip.

2 Yes. It's good for someone to tell you about a place. For .... , we walked round some places in Athens without one and we were really confused.

3 In my .... , it's good to go with your parents because they pay for everything!

4 Yes, sometimes. .... example, I bought a poster of a coffee cup in Rome for my friend because she loves coffee!

5 Read the discussion questions (A–D). Match the answers 1–4 in Ex 4 with the questions.

A Do you usually buy presents when you're on holiday? Why / Why not? ....

B What's your favourite present that you've received from someone who's been on holiday? Why? ....

C Do you think it's a good idea to have a guide when you visit famous places? Or would you prefer to look round by yourself? Why? ....

D Would you prefer a trip with your school or a trip with your family? Why? ....

6 🄴 Read the task below again. Think about your opinion of each present. Record your comments on each present and choose which would be the best. Listen to your recording and check:

1 Did you give a reason why each object would or would not make a good present?

2 Did you use phrases from Ex 4 to give your opinion and examples?

A present to take home

WRITING

a story

1 Complete the comments about writing a good story.

1 Write an interesting .... because then people will want to read more of your story.

2 Try to have a surprising or funny .... , so that the reader will remember it and think your story was worth reading.

3 Use different .... like *amazing, dangerous, exciting.*

4 Use .... like *carefully, quickly, suddenly* to describe how people do things.

5 Use .... expressions so the reader can follow the sequence of events.

2 Decide whether the sentences are part of the beginning (B), middle (M) or end (E) of a story.

1 After dinner we all went outside for a walk along the beach. ....

2 Yesterday, everyone got up early because we were excited about our holiday. ....

3 Unfortunately, it was the wrong time. The restaurant was closed! ....

4 I'll never forget her happy face when she opened the present. ....

5 It was the final day of our holiday and we were all sad. ....

6 While Mum parked the car, Dad checked into the hotel. ....

3 Reorder the words to make sentences with adverbs. There may be more than one possible answer.

1 car / drove / the / slowly / Mum

....

2 went / the / suddenly / room / dark

....

3 the / quickly / email / typed / he

....

4 piano / the / she / beautifully / played

....

5 spoke / sadly / he

....

6 at / angrily / screen / the / shouted / man / the

....

7 the / you / go / to / immediately / doctor / must

....

8 very / on / the / loudly / she / phone / speaks

....

4 Read the writing task and the story. Answer the questions.

> Your English teacher has asked you to write a story. Your story must begin with this sentence.
>
> **Kelly and her family were really excited about the car trip into the hills.**

Kelly and her family were really excited about the car trip into the hills. They all sang loudly. Her mum had the sandwiches and the map and gave Kelly's dad directions. The sun was shining and they were all happy.

Suddenly the road started to climb up a hill. The view was amazing. After half an hour Kelly's mum said, 'We're lost!' At first, they laughed. It was an adventure. But then it started to rain heavily. The road became wet and dangerous, and her dad couldn't see clearly. They stopped singing.

Finally, Kelly's mum saw a road sign to their hotel. When they got there, they ate their sandwiches in the car park. No more driving!

1 How many paragraphs are there? ....

2 List the adjectives in the story: ....

....

3 List the adverbs: ....

....

4 List the time expressions: ....

....

5 Read the task again and plan your own story. Remember to:

1 divide your story into three parts (beginning, middle, end).

2 make notes for each part.

3 use different adjectives and adverbs.

4 use time expressions and past tenses.

5 think of a good ending.

6 **e** Write your story in about 100 words. Read it and check it for any spelling, punctuation or grammar mistakes.

UNIT CHECK

1 Complete the sentences in the present perfect form.

1 I / read / a lot of English books.

....

2 my brother / not be / to the USA.

....

3 How many superhero films / you / see?

....

4 my dad / have / five cars in his life!

....

5 some of my classmates / not do / all the homework.

....

6 your mum / meet / all our teachers?

....

2 Put the words in the correct places in the sentences.

1 Kim has arrived. She says 'hello'! (just)

....

2 Have your parents been to Norway? (ever)

....

3 Who shall I invite to the party? I've asked Mark because I saw him at school today. (already)

....

4 Have you done your packing? (yet)

....

5 I've eaten insects! Have you? (never)

....

6 We haven't been to the museum but we're going tomorrow. (yet)

....

3 Complete the sentences with *for* or *since*.

1 Our teacher's been at this school .... eleven years.

2 I haven't spoken to Gary .... we came back from holiday.

3 I've been playing this game .... 6 o'clock.

4 My friend has lived in this town .... she was five years old.

5 We've had the same geography teacher .... two years.

6 I haven't texted Fran .... a long time.

7 We went to Spain .... two weeks this summer. It was amazing!

8 I've haven't played chess .... my grandpa visited. We always play together.

4 Find the wrong word or phrase in each group.

1 hotel: guest fare reception booking

2 airport: customs security accommodation visa

3 train station: passenger return ticket platform guide

5 Complete the blog with the correct words.

___

booking customs got ID luggage paid passengers
security tourists travelled

___

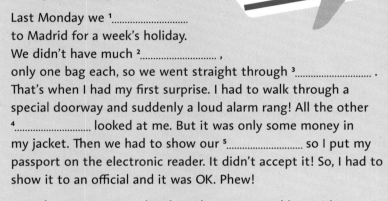

A nightmare journey

Last Monday we ¹........................... to Madrid for a week's holiday. We didn't have much ²........................... , only one bag each, so we went straight through ³........................... . That's when I had my first surprise. I had to walk through a special doorway and suddenly a loud alarm rang! All the other ⁴........................... looked at me. But it was only some money in my jacket. Then we had to show our ⁵........................... so I put my passport on the electronic reader. It didn't accept it! So, I had to show it to an official and it was OK. Phew!

But when we got onto the plane there was a problem with our ⁶........................... and we couldn't sit together. And when we got off the plane the ⁷........................... official opened and searched our cases!

We ⁸........................... a taxi to take us to the hotel but it took ages because there were lots of ⁹........................... walking in the road taking photographs. Dad ¹⁰........................... more than he expected for the ride. Mum was really angry!

What a journey!

6 Choose the correct words to complete the complaints from customers about their holidays.

1 The brochure said everything was included but we had to pay the taxi **journey / fare** from the airport to the hotel.

2 The instructions told us to wait on **platform / station** 10 but the information was wrong and we missed the train.

3 There wasn't a **return / fare** ticket in our travel pack so we had to pay extra to get home.

4 There were too many **tourists / passengers** for our plane and we had to wait for the next one.

5 There was never anyone in the hotel **room / reception**. We had to wait ages sometimes to get our room keys.

6 The plane fare didn't include **tickets / luggage** so we had to pay extra for our suitcases.

7 We decided to book nice **accommodation / fare** because we knew we'd be tired when we arrived.

8 Getting through **ID / customs** took longer than we expected because there was a problem with someone else's bag in front of us.

What's your idea of fun?

READING

1 Complete the online posts with the correct words.

> arranging   beeps   download   give it a go
> staring at

More and more families are ¹.......................... **to go on screen-free holidays, where phones, tablets and computers are all banned. Could you survive a holiday without your phone?**

EricaJon34 — I'd certainly be happy to ².......................... . I think it might be cool to try it for a week or two!

Tara_London — No way! When my phone ³.......................... , I know that I'm connected with my friends. I'd be lost without it!

MattyB — Yes, why not! Doing exciting things on holiday is more fun than ⁴.......................... a screen!

Chocofan_Sam — Noooooo! Don't take my phone away! I need to ⁵.......................... music and watch films and chat to my friends!

2 **e** Read the notice and message. Choose the correct answers (A–C).

1

Screen-free zone

Please note, this holiday accommodation is screen-free and there is no internet access anywhere on the site. A phone signal is available in the reception area, but please use in emergencies only.

A Guests cannot use the internet or their phones anywhere on the site.

B Guests can use their phones in their rooms in an emergency.

C It is possible to make important phone calls in the reception area.

2

> Hi Abi, my parents are taking me on a screen-free holiday next week. Can you lend me some books so I don't get too bored? I'll text you when I get home.
>
> Thanks, Sara

Why has Sara sent this text?

A because she's feeling bored

B because she wants to borrow something

C because she won't be able to text her friends next week

3 Read about Luke's holiday experience. Who has he written the article for?

A a holiday review website

B teachers and parents

C other teenagers

4 **e** **Read the text again. Choose the correct answers.**

1 When Luke's dad first suggested a tech-free holiday, Luke

   A didn't feel very excited about it.

   B felt nervous about being without his phone.

   C was annoyed at the idea of not taking his phone.

   D thought it might be an interesting experience.

2 Luke found it easy to forget about his phone in the mountains because

   A there was no internet connection.

   B he was enjoying being in such beautiful countryside.

   C there were lots of people to talk to.

   D it was right at the bottom of his backpack.

3 In the third paragraph, what did Luke find surprising about the holiday?

   A He didn't enjoy all the activities.

   B He and his family didn't talk very much.

   C He saw a lot of amazing wild animals.

   D The holiday seemed to last a long time.

4 Now that he is back home, Luke

   A uses his phone less than he did before.

   B gets better results at school.

   C spends more time chatting to his parents.

   D sometimes finds his phone annoying.

5 What might Luke's mum say about the holiday?

   A Both kids complained about not having a phone for the whole car journey from home to the mountains!

   B I liked the idea of a tech-free holiday, but in fact the kids just spent all their time arguing!

   C I loved staying in the hut and being close to the river, and the fish were delicious!

   D The climbing and hiking were great fun, and seeing wild cats was amazing!

5 **Complete the meanings with the words and expressions in bold in the text.**

1 When you are .... on something, you are making an effort to think about it.

2 If you .... that something is true, you say or agree that it is true, even if you don't want it to be true.

3 When you have .... with someone, you talk or write to them.

4 When you .... a phone or tablet, you stop it from working.

5 If there is a .... of something, there isn't any, or there isn't enough.

6 If something is .... , it is likely to happen.

Luke Abbot talks about his tech-free holiday experience

We all know it's impossible to live without your phone, right? So I was surprised when my dad suggested a tech-free family holiday. The holiday itself sounded really exciting, staying in a small hut in the mountains, hiking, boating and climbing every day. But no phones? My sister was definitely not pleased at the thought of no **contact** with friends for three weeks, but I was curious to know what it would be like, and willing to give it a go.

It was certainly strange to **switch off** my phone and leave it behind as we left for the airport, knowing I wouldn't be able to talk to people back home. I must **admit** I considered hiding it in my backpack, until dad told us that there was no phone signal or internet in the mountains! But once we got there, the scenery was so spectacular in all directions that I soon found I'd forgotten all about home and friends and didn't miss my phone beeping in my pocket every two minutes.

The days passed amazingly quickly. We took our boats over fast-moving parts of the river (scary, but fun!) and explored steep mountain paths where bears and wild cats had been, although we didn't see any. We caught fish in the river and cooked them over open fires. We didn't chat as much as I expected because we were usually busy **concentrating** on what we were doing. But despite the **lack** of conversation we all became closer to each other, even me and my sister, who argue all the time at home.

So what was it like coming home? I think my parents secretly hoped that my sister and I might continue tech-free and put all our efforts into improving our school grades. But that wasn't a **realistic** idea. I probably spend as much time on my phone now as I did before, but I know when to put it down, and it annoys me if friends use theirs when I'm talking to them. The whole family hangs out together a lot more now and we discuss all kinds of things, which is great. So don't be scared of being tech-free for a while – there is life beyond the phone!

GRAMMAR

zero and first conditionals

1 Match the sentence halves.

1 When I have nothing better to do,

2 If we don't leave now,

3 I usually stay at home

4 If you go to that website,

5 If I take a good photo,

6 We'll have a barbecue

A if the weather's nice tomorrow.

B you'll find lots of information on local activities.

C I usually watch a movie.

D I always post it online.

E when it rains.

F we'll be late for the concert.

2 Look at the sentences in Ex 1. Decide if they are zero conditional (0) or first conditional (1).

1 .... **3** .... **5** ....

2 .... **4** .... **6** ....

3 🔊 9.1 Choose the correct verb forms in the conversations. Listen and check.

1 A: What **¹will you / do you** usually do at the weekend if you **²don't have / won't have** any homework?

B: When I **³have / 'll have** free time, I **⁴work / 'll work** as a volunteer at a pet rescue centre. I love animals!

2 A: What are your plans for the weekend?

B: If it **⁵'s / 'll be** warm, I **⁶go / 'll go** sailing with my dad – it's great fun!

A: And what **⁷will you do / do you do** if the weather **⁸isn't / won't be** good?

B: I'll probably watch sport on TV!

3 A: I need to go home now. My parents **⁹are / will be** annoyed if I **¹⁰m / 'll be** late.

B: I know what you mean! My mum always **¹¹gets / will get** worried when I **¹²don't get / won't get** home on time.

4 A: When I **¹³feel / will feel** bored, I always **¹⁴will watch / watch** a movie.

B: That's a good idea. I **¹⁵try / 'll try** that next time I **¹⁶have / 'll have** nothing to do!

5 A: I don't feel like cooking. If you **¹⁷'ll make / make** us dinner tonight, I **¹⁸wash / 'll wash** the dishes.

B: OK, I **¹⁹make / 'll make** something when I **²⁰will finish / finish** this game.

4 Write the zero or first conditional sentences.

1 I / get / annoyed / at school / if / my lessons / be / boring

....

2 I / text / you / when / I / arrive / at the cinema

....

3 if / you / not tell / people / about your party / they / not come

.... !

4 when / my friends / come round / we / usually play / computer games

....

5 if / I / not have / much homework / this evening / I / go swimming

....

6 I / always / feel / bored / when / my friends / be / away on holiday

....

5 Complete the text with the correct verb forms. Use the zero or first conditional.

Have **fun**

Being bored is bad for you!

Scientists have found that when people **¹**........................... (be) bored for long periods of time, their health **²**........................... (start) to suffer. Clearly, this **³**........................... (not be) true if you only **⁴**........................... (feel) bored in the occasional maths lesson, like I do. But it's definitely a good reason to find something fun to do every day. And maybe it's something to think about for the future, too. It seems that if you **⁵**........................... (choose) a job you enjoy, you **⁶**........................... (stay) happier and healthier through your life, but if you **⁷**........................... (do) a job you find boring, you **⁸**........................... (not be) as happy, and you **⁹**........................... (have) more health problems. So it's good news really – fun is good for you as well as being … fun!

6 What makes you feel bored? What do you do if you feel bored?

....

....

....

VOCABULARY

entertainment and technology

1 Choose the three words and phrases that go with each verb.

1 You can listen to **a song / a live band / a connection / a link / a podcast.**

2 You can have **a sport / a sleepover / chess / wi-fi in your hotel / a good time.**

3 You can do **a search / a track / a quiz / a computer game / ballet.**

4 You can watch **an action film / a search / a video / a link / TV.**

5 You can play **the piano / a vlog / a computer game / a website / tennis.**

6 You can download **a film / an app / a song / a good connection / a search.**

2 Complete the crossword. Then unscramble the shaded letters to solve the final clue.

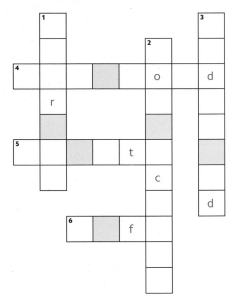

Across

4 You use these secret letters to access social media.

5 to remove something from your phone or computer

6 Most hotels have this, so you can use the internet.

Down

1 You need this to give your phone more power.

2 the way your phone or tablet is joined to the internet

3 This means you can watch TV programmes when you want.

7 Clue: You need this to make a call on your phone.

....

3 🔊 9.2 Complete what people say about their problems. Listen and check.

1 I need to call my friend, but I can't switch my phone on. I was using it all morning, and now there's no power left. My b_ _ _ _ _ _ i_ d_ _ _ .

2 I want to get onto this website, but I can't. It keeps asking me for my secret word and I can't remember it. I've f_ _ _ _ _ _ _ m_ p_ _ _ _ _ _ .

3 I really want to download this app, but I've already got lots of apps on my phone, and it's full. I've r_ _ o_ _ o_ m_ _ _ _ .

4 It's really difficult to watch films on my tablet at home. They keep stopping. It's so annoying! We don't h_ _ _ a g_ _ _ c_ _ _ _ _ _ _ _ .

5 It's my birthday soon, so I want to invite some of my friends to come to my house. My parents say it's OK for them to come and watch a film, but not to stay the night. They won't let me h_ _ _ a s_ _ _ _ _ _ _ .

Extend

4 Read the blog post and match the underlined words with the meanings.

1 become joined to something ....

2 switched on ....

3 permission to use the internet ....

4 download software or an app onto your phone or computer ....

5 typed it onto a phone or computer ....

I'm on holiday, staying in a hotel in a small village, miles from anywhere. Last night, my brother and I wanted to play a new computer game, so we asked for the password to get <u>access</u> to the internet. We got the password and <u>entered it</u>, and started getting excited about the game, but we couldn't believe how slow the internet was! It took us about 15 minutes just to <u>connect</u> to the wi-fi. I tried to <u>install</u> the game onto my tablet, and that took about half an hour. Then the power went off, and when I <u>turned</u> my tablet <u>on</u> again, the game had disappeared. In the end, we decided to play cards instead! Take my advice – when you're miles from the nearest town, with the slowest wi-fi in the world, take a low-tech form of entertainment!

LISTENING

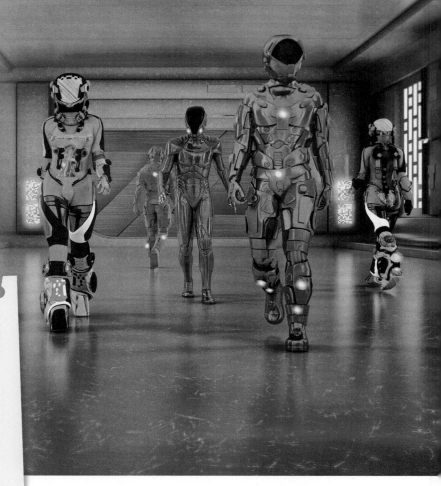

1 🔊 9.3 You will hear a teacher talking about a science fiction convention. What is he giving information about?

A his own experiences of a science fiction convention

B a school visit to a science fiction convention

C plans for organising a science fiction convention at the school

2 e 🔊 9.4 Listen again. For each question, write the correct answer in the gap. Write one or two words, a date or a time.

Trip to science fiction convention

The bus will leave the school at ¹............................ on Saturday morning.

Students should bring ².......................... with them.

There is a ³.......................... in the afternoon.

The teacher recommends buying ⁴.......................... at the convention.

Students should meet at the ⁵.......................... at the end of the day.

There will be a prize for the best ⁶.......................... on the school website.

3 Read the sentences that the teacher said. Match the words in bold with the meanings.

1 The **queues** for food are always quite long.

2 There's a movie make-up **display** in the morning.

3 It's worth **looking** at the books.

4 I'm going to **post** some information about our trip on the school website.

5 You can **upload** your favourite photo.

A to write something online

B an arrangement of things for people to look at

C lines of people waiting for something

D it's a good idea to do this

E to put a picture or piece of writing onto a website

verb patterns: *-ing* and *to*-infinitive

4 Complete the parts of reviews of the science fiction convention with the correct form of the verbs in brackets.

B|W|A **Ben Waylon Academy**
convention reviews

Josh Taylor, year 7

The convention is great for science fiction fans, but it's also good if you're interested in ¹.......................... (learn) about real science, like space travel. I really enjoyed ².......................... (see) all the amazing costumes. I'm definitely hoping ³.......................... (dress up) when I go again next year!

Emma Jones, year 8

It's important ⁴.......................... (plan) your day carefully because there's so much to see and there isn't time for everything. Also, if you're like me and hate ⁵.......................... (wait) in queues, you need to make sure you get there early for events you really want ⁶.......................... (attend).

Shona Barclay, year 7

It was amazing ⁷.......................... (meet) other people who love science fiction as much as I do. I'd like to thank Mr Smithson for ⁸.......................... (organise) the trip!

SPEAKING

1 🔊 9.5 **Look at photo A and listen to a student describing it. Tick the things she talks about.**

People ☐   Clothes ☐
Place ☐   Activity ☐
Weather ☐   Feelings ☐

2 🔊 9.6 **Choose the correct words to complete the sentences about photo A. Listen and check.**

1 **There are / It's** five people in the photo.

2 Most of the friends **eat / are eating** a sandwich.

3 The friends are **standing / sitting** on the grass.

4 The two girls in the photo **have / are having** long hair.

5 There are some buildings and trees **behind / beside** them.

6 There are some books **under / in front of** them.

3 **Complete the sentences for guessing about photo A with the correct words.**

look	maybe	might	probably	think

1 I guess it's .... summer because they aren't wearing coats.

2 They .... be students.

3 .... it's their lunch break.

4 They .... very happy.

5 I .... they're good friends.

4 🔊 9.7 **Match the halves of the sentences the student uses when she doesn't know the word. Listen and check.**

1 I can't ....
2 I'm not ....
3 It goes ....
4 I don't ....
5 It's a kind ....
6 It's something ....

A sure of the word in English.
B on your arm.
C remember the word in English.
D of plant.
E know the word in English.
F you grow around your house.

5 **Look at photo B. Make notes about it.**

People: ....
Place: ....
Weather: ....
Clothes: ....
Activity: ....
Feelings: ....

6 🔊 9.8 **Practise describing the photo. Record yourself.**

WRITING

an email

1 Read the email task. Match the four notes (1–4) with the four things you have to do in your reply (A–D).

> Read this email from your English-speaking friend Sam, and the notes you have made. Write your email to Ali, using all the notes.

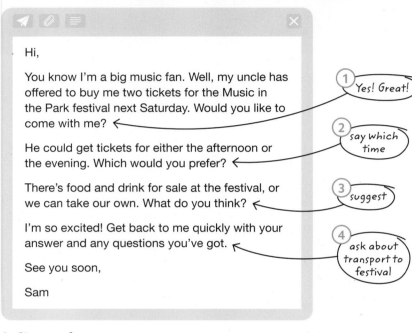

Hi,

You know I'm a big music fan. Well, my uncle has offered to buy me two tickets for the Music in the Park festival next Saturday. Would you like to come with me? ← ① *Yes! Great!*

He could get tickets for either the afternoon or the evening. Which would you prefer? ← ② *say which time*

There's food and drink for sale at the festival, or we can take our own. What do you think? ← ③ *suggest*

I'm so excited! Get back to me quickly with your answer and any questions you've got. ← ④ *ask about transport to festival*

See you soon,

Sam

A Give a preference. ....
B Make a suggestion. ....
C Ask a question. ....
D Accept an invitation. ....

2 Look at note 2 in Sam's email again, then read the three possible ways of responding (1–3) below. Match them with the descriptions (A–C). Then circle which is the best way of responding.

(1) I think I'd rather go in the evening. I usually play football on Saturday afternoon and my team has got a very important game next Saturday. We're doing well this year, and I really enjoy playing!

(2) I'd prefer to go in the evening.

(3) I'd rather go in the evening because all the good bands usually play in the evening.

A It gives a preference, but it uses the same words as in the notes and does not add any more information.
B It gives a preference, but it adds too much extra information and the information has no connection.
C It gives a preference using different words, and it adds some relevant information.

3 Look at note 3 in Sam's email again. Choose three points that might be relevant in a reply.

1 My sister is a vegetarian. ☐
2 It's cheaper to take our own food. ☐
3 There are usually some great food stalls at festivals. ☐
4 I always have ice cream when I go out for the day with my parents. ☐
5 It's heavy to carry food and drink. ☐
6 I had some really nice food at a drama festival last year with my cousins. ☐

4 Choose the correct words to complete the sentences. Then match each sentence (1–6) with a function (A–D). Some functions match more than one sentence.

1 I'd rather **buy** / **to buy** / **buying** some food when we're there.
2 Thanks for **invite** / **to invite** / **inviting** me to your party. I'd love **come** / **to come** / **coming**.
3 Shall we **get** / **to get** / **getting** the bus together?
4 How about **meet** / **to meet** / **meeting** at my house at two o'clock?
5 I'd prefer **go** / **to go** / **going** on Saturday.
6 I'm sorry I can't **come** / **to come** / **coming** to the party. I need **spend** / **to spend** / **spending** some time with my grandparents.

A making a suggestion ....
B giving a preference ....
C accepting an invitation ....
D refusing an invitation ....

5 Look at the task in Ex 1 again and plan your email. Use the plan below.

Email beginning	
Note 1	
Note 2	
Note 3	
Note 4	
Email ending	

6 **e** Use your notes and write your email. Write about 100 words.

UNIT CHECK

1 Complete the message with the correct words. There are three words you don't need.

> charge   charger   dead   delete   do   get
> have   listen   memory   play   wi-fi

< Back

Help! I'm sending this secretly. My parents have decided that Saturdays are now family days and are screen-free! Can you believe it? They won't let me ¹........................... computer games or even ²........................... to music on my phone! Today they took us out for the day. I secretly put my phone in my bag, but there was no free ³........................... in the place we went to, and I couldn't ⁴........................... a phone signal! I'm back home now, but my battery's nearly ⁵........................... , and my parents have taken away my ⁶........................... so I can't ⁷........................... it again. Please can someone invite me to ⁸........................... a sleepover with them next Saturday?

2 Read the advertisement. Choose the correct words to complete it.

Try the new
Jansong X500
tablet

It's a super-powerful tablet, so you can ¹**download** / **watch** all your favourite apps and you'll never have to ²**forget** / **delete** any because you'll never run out of ³**signal** / **memory**. Perfect for watching TV ⁴**on demand** / **for demand**. It's so fast it can do ⁵**looks** / **searches** online in half the time of other tablets. The new 5E technology means you will always have a good ⁶**link** / **connection**! Fingerprint security means that you don't need a ⁷**password** / **click** to unlock your phone. It also comes with free ⁸**tracks** / **headphones** so you can listen to music without disturbing others.

3 Complete the sentences with the correct words.

> access   connect   enter   install   turn on

1 Will you help me .... this new game on my laptop?
2 There are revision notes on the school website, but you need a password to get .... to them.
3 You shouldn't .... your personal details unless you know the website is safe.
4 You can use our wi-fi to .... to the internet.
5 To start using your new tablet, simply .... the device and follow the instructions on the screen.

4 Complete the zero and first conditional sentences with the correct form of the verbs.

1 I always .... (go) round to my friend's house when I .... (feel) bored.
2 If you .... (spend) all your time playing computer games, you .... (not do) well in your exams!
3 I .... (come) with you to the amusement park on Sunday if I .... (finish) all my homework on Saturday.
4 If the weather .... (be) nice, I usually .... (cycle) to school.
5 Lots of people .... (come) to this beach when it .... (be) sunny.
6 If you .... (not like) the present, I .... (take) it back to the shop and change it for you.

5 Choose the correct verb forms to complete the online forum.

Why do you geocache?

Thompson2

Evening, everyone. We've just decided ¹**to start** / **starting** geocaching and we'd love ²**to know** / **knowing**, why do *you* geocache?

Jesles

We enjoy ³**to find** / **finding** really interesting places to hide things. And then it's interesting ⁴**to see** / **seeing** how quickly other people find them!

Jamjar

You have to be good at ⁵**to think** / **thinking** of interesting things to hide. That's the fun part. It's also good for ⁶**meet** / **meeting** new people. I've made a lot of new friends through geocaching.

Silsee

Imagine ⁷**to open** / **opening** a secret box, not knowing what's inside – that's the fun of geocaching! I love everything about it! I only started a few months ago, and now it's impossible ⁸**to stop** / **stopping** me!

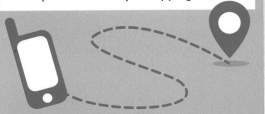

REVIEW: UNITS 1–9

1 Join the sentences with a relative clause using *who* or *which*.

1 A waiter served us. She was very friendly.
The waiter .... very friendly.

2 She showed us the menu. It was really interesting.
The menu .... really interesting.

3 There were lots of vegetable dishes. They were suitable for vegetarians.
There were lots of vegetable dishes .... for vegetarians.

4 The chef is excellent. He works there.
The chef .... excellent.

5 The customers seem happy. They eat there.
The customers .... happy.

6 You can read reviews online. They are all very good.
The reviews .... all very good.

2 Complete the posts with the correct words. There is one word you don't need.

burned   cooked   raw   salty   sour   spicy   sweet

Do things ever go wrong when you're cooking?
Tell us your stories!

I once tried making a chocolate cake. The oven was too hot, so it was all black and ¹.................... on the outside but not properly ².................... in the middle!

I made some biscuits once, but I added the sugar twice by mistake. They were much too ³.................... and no one could eat them!

I had a go at making a lemon drink last summer, to keep me cool. I forgot to add any sugar, so it was too ⁴.................... to drink!

I tried cooking some fish last week. I put it in the oven, but didn't turn the oven on. When I took it out half an hour later, it was still ⁵....................!

I made a pizza once and thought it would be good to add some chilli. It was so ⁶.................... that none of my friends wanted to eat it!

3 Complete the recipe with adverbs formed from the adjectives in brackets.

| Home | Recent Posts | Profile | | Subscribe |

How to make perfect ice cream

As you know, I love ice cream, and I've found that you can make delicious ice cream really ¹.................... (easy) with a machine called an ice cream maker. Pour some cream into the machine and add sugar ².................... (slow), bit by bit. Allow time for the machine to mix it in ³.................... (good). Then add fruit or chocolate. Do this ⁴.................... (careful). If you add it too ⁵.................... (quick), it might spill and make a mess. It's important to try ⁶.................... (hard) to keep your parents' kitchen clean! Then leave the machine for about half an hour until your ice cream is ready. Simple! Eat it ⁷.................... (immediate) and enjoy!

4 Write sentences using the present perfect. For questions 3–6, add the word in brackets in the correct place.

1 my uncle / do / lots of amazing things
....

3 I / not / travel / by plane / before
....

3 you / try / water skiing (ever)
.... ?

4 it / start / raining (just)
....

5 we / spend / a lot of money / on this holiday (already)
....

6 you / finish / eating (yet)
.... ?

5 Choose the correct words to complete the tips.

Tips for TRAVELLERS

★ Think about the countries you are going to visit. You may need to apply for a **¹visa / reservation / fare** to go to some countries.

★ Think about where you are going to stay. It's a good idea to book your **²security / accommodation / journey** before you leave. Remember, you can often make **³customs / reservations / tickets** online.

★ If you need to **⁴go / travel / catch** a train, get your ticket in advance, then you won't have to pay the full **⁵fare / ticket / trip**. When you get to the station, check which **⁶booking / return / platform** your train leaves from.

★ If you're travelling by plane, allow plenty of time to get through **⁷visa / security / reception** at the airport. You don't want to miss your flight!

6 Complete the advice with the correct form of the verbs. Use the zero or first conditional.

Do you find it difficult to get started on your homework?

Our readers offer their advice

- Plan something nice to do afterwards. If I
¹........................... (have) something to look forward to,
I ²........................... (find) it easier to do my homework
quickly.

- Listen to some music. If you ³........................... (do) that,
you ⁴........................... (soon be) more cheerful and in a
better mood for homework.

- Think about the future, not the present. When
I ⁵........................... (not want) to do my homework,
I ⁶........................... (look) at university websites. That
makes me want to work harder!

- Divide the work into smaller bits. If you ⁷...........................
(see) your homework as one huge piece of work, you
⁸........................... (never get) started. It's easier if you do
it one small bit at a time!

7 Complete the sentences with the correct form of the verbs.

1 I've decided .... (learn) how to play chess.

2 My sister is really good at .... (paint).

3 I'm happy .... (help) with the party if you want me to.

4 I can't imagine .... (live) in a small village where there's nothing to do!

5 I practise .... (do) card tricks every day.

6 My parents won't allow me .... (invite) friends round during the week.

8 Match the halves of the phrases.

1	do	A	your password for a website
2	play	B	a sleepover with some friends
3	have	C	a search online
4	download	D	memory on your phone
5	run out of	E	an app onto your phone
6	forget	F	the guitar

9 **e** For each question, write one word in the gap.

The Old Scottish Lighthouse

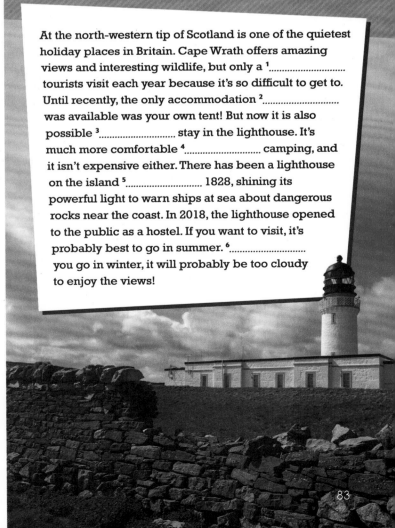

At the north-western tip of Scotland is one of the quietest holiday places in Britain. Cape Wrath offers amazing views and interesting wildlife, but only a ¹........................... tourists visit each year because it's so difficult to get to. Until recently, the only accommodation ²........................... was available was your own tent! But now it is also possible ³........................... stay in the lighthouse. It's much more comfortable ⁴........................... camping, and it isn't expensive either. There has been a lighthouse on the island ⁵........................... 1828, shining its powerful light to warn ships at sea about dangerous rocks near the coast. In 2018, the lighthouse opened to the public as a hostel. If you want to visit, it's probably best to go in summer. ⁶........................... you go in winter, it will probably be too cloudy to enjoy the views!

READING

Part 1

Questions 1–5

For each question, choose the correct answer.

---

(1)

School Talent Show

Make sure entries for this Friday evening's Talent Show reach me by end of school Thursday or you won't be able to perform. A list of the judging categories is below.

Mr Turner

A Students must give their names for the Talent Show at least twenty-four hours before.

B Students who have entered the Talent Show and can't perform must inform Mr Turner.

C Students wanting to enter the Talent Show should sign their names here.

(2)

London Trip

Details of the May London trip for Year 10s now available on school website, with booking form to complete. Trip accompanied by Mr Parks and Miss Draper. Early booking is advised as places are limited.

A Not all students in Year 10 will be able to go to London.

B Year 10 students have until May to book a place on the London trip.

C Year 10 students should ask their teachers for information about the trip.

3

To: Class 9D
From: Helena

Jacky now collecting for our teacher's leaving present. Hoping to collect £50! Message me with suggestions for gift. Asking people to sign the card – with Pete C now.

A Students need to give presents for their teacher to Helena.

B Students should send Helena ideas about what to buy their teacher.

C Students should give their cards for the teacher to one of their classmates.

4

History Essays

History essays are due in by 4.30 Thursday. Click on link below to upload. As usual, essays received after this time will be marked down.

A Students who are late more than once will lose marks.

B Students should give history essays to the teacher in Thursday's class.

C Students must submit their history essays online.

5

School Prizegiving Ceremony

Planning to bring more than 2 guests to Prizegiving? Please inform the School Office, or there may be seating problems. Remind your guests to arrive on time to allow a quick start.

A It is essential for guests to arrive early to find a seat.

B It is important to tell school if you're attending Prizegiving.

C It is necessary to tell the school if you are bringing multiple guests.

Part 2

Questions 6–10

For each question, choose the correct answer.

....

The young people below all want to go to a summer festival next weekend. On the next page there are descriptions of eight festivals. Decide which festival would be most suitable for the people below.

6 Wendy loves music and sings and dances. She'd like to improve her skills and get onstage herself. She's got the whole weekend free.

7 Greg is fourteen and wants to be an author one day. He'd like to go to a book festival for the weekend and as he has very little money he'd like it to be free.

8 Danny wants his French friend to see some English traditions. They've got Sunday free but have a family birthday party in the early evening. They'd like to travel there by public transport.

9 Annie has no money but wants to go to an event on Saturday where she can see different types of entertainment. She likes being in a crowd and her dad will pick her up when she's ready.

10 Billy is just fifteen and wants to spend some birthday money on learning something. He's interested in different kinds of engines and vehicles.

A Dibden Festival

This year's book festival will be our twentieth! To celebrate, ten big-name authors will talk about their latest books and on Saturday afternoon there will be a special session for Young Adult fiction where you can ask questions about your favourite characters. As always, there will be book sales and book swap opportunities. Only £15 entrance fee for the weekend.

B Queen's Teen Arts Festival

Want your hobby to be your career? At the Teen Arts Festival in Portsmouth's Queen's Theatre this weekend you can perform for others and for the experts, who will give you advice. On Saturday evening there will be a concert with professional performers and on Sunday you rehearse and perform a concert yourselves!

C Country fair

Bring your family to Westchurch Country Fair this weekend! Only £10 per day, including parking! Two minutes from bus stop and five from the train. Listen to country songs and watch folk dancing performed in costume by Westchurch school children. Lots of local pottery, paintings and food to buy and a special pet competition for the children!

D Tamworth Festival

Always got your head in a novel? Got some stories of your own to tell? At our festival for young writers on Saturday and Sunday (no admission fee for under 15s) you can listen to other teens reading their work and join discussion groups with famous writers to get some advice. Why not enter the 'Speedy Writers' competition on Sunday for 12–17-year-olds? There's a £450 prize!

E The Ravensburgh Show

Expect excitement, noise and big crowds at the Ravensburgh Air Show this weekend. For £25 you can watch planes old and new perform amazing acrobatics in the sky. Also, a chance for trips in some of the planes for those holding a 'lucky ticket'. Cheap flying lessons for 14-year-olds upwards. See you there!

F Linwood Park

A young person is wanted to work at our care home for four hours on Saturday and Sunday afternoons. The job requires you to make tea and fetch snacks for our elderly residents, as well as sit and chat to them. All our assistants must have basic kitchen skills.

G Davis House Show

Love speed? The supercar display show on Sunday (entrance £20), with the chance of talking to some famous racing drivers should not be missed! Crowded? – yes! Noisy? – definitely! Over 16? For £30 you could take a supercar round the track yourself!

H Lyndhurst Day

The year's most special event takes place in Lyndhurst this Saturday – the carnival! Local people have been preparing costumes for this all year and the bands and dancers, as well as the magic shows along the High Street, will be exciting, colourful and loud! Starts at 2.30 and there is no entry fee. Expect lots of people and public transport delays in the area until at least 8.30 p.m.

Part 3

Questions 11–15

For each question, choose the correct answer.

Photography and me

Photography competition winner, Charlie Moon, writes about his hobby.

I'd never been very interested in entering competitions. I didn't think it was important to show that you're better than everyone else. So, I think I surprised people, especially my parents, when I went in for a national photography competition for young photographers! The prize money was an attraction – £1,000! However, I'd decided that if I wanted a future career in photography, I needed to learn to be a bit competitive. I might have a good camera and be able to take great photographs, but in the future I'd need to beat other photographers for jobs!

It was my friend who told me about the competition. I went onto the website and entered and immediately started to worry that people might not like my photos. Then, when I saw the other entries I couldn't believe how good they were! But I won and it taught me a lot.

People often ask me why I started photography in the first place. Lots of my family are into photography. It's my uncle's job and there are copies of his photographs all over our house! I suppose I got interested when I got a cheap camera for my birthday when I was five. I learned how to take basic photographs, and that was it. It wasn't a digital camera, so it cost my parents a lot of money to buy film for it and then get the photographs printed!

Now, of course, it's different. Because of modern technology people don't need to spend a lot on expensive cameras. Anyone can take good photos with their phone or tablet and they can download software to play around with the pictures. It's great that it's not just a hobby for a few people any more. But I still think that it's amazing to hold a real old-fashioned camera in your hands or put it on a stand. I hope that doesn't change. One thing that is important for me is printing out my best photos. Lots of people store everything online, but printing and hanging up a photograph makes it very special, and they look great!

Photography is a cool hobby to have for people like me who like art and technology. You can join a photography club. The one I'm in encourages us to take photos indoors and outdoors. And, I think differently about competitions now – they can be really good fun!

---

11 The reason Charlie entered the competition was to
  A get money for new equipment.
  B impress his family.
  C get some experience.
  D improve his skills.

12 How did Charlie feel when he entered the competition?
  A confident about winning
  B excited that people would see his pictures
  C proud that his pictures were good
  D surprised at other people's talent

13 What encouraged Charlie to take up photography when he was young?
  A He wanted to copy his uncle.
  B He received a gift.
  C He was surrounded by family photos.
  D He had some extra money to spend.

14 What does Charlie think about new technology for photography?
  A It encourages more people to take photos.
  B It means the quality of photographs is worse than before.
  C It has stopped people keeping their photographs for a long time.
  D It is always changing and improving.

15 What might Charlie's uncle say?
  A 'When I visit Charlie and his family I always like looking at his latest photos. It's good he hangs his favourites on the wall.'
  B 'Charlie is a really good photographer and did so well in the competition, but he would be better if he joined a club.'
  C 'I'm glad Charlie took my advice and entered the competition. It's really given him confidence.'
  D 'Charlie does well with all this new, modern equipment but I'd like to see him use something a bit more traditional. I think he'd learn a lot.'

Part 4

Questions 16–20

Five sentences have been removed from the text below.

For each question, choose the correct answer.

There are three extra sentences which you do not need to use.

The big night!

By Gina Williams, 14

Last Friday was the first night of our school play and on Wednesday I started to get nervous. Everyone was talking about how excited they were, but I was scared because I was playing the main character. **16**........ That Wednesday night I didn't get much sleep.

We spent Thursday evening getting the stage ready and being busy helped my nerves. The play happens inside an old house and we had to build walls with windows in them. **17**........ Everything looked very realistic.

Then it was Friday evening and we put on our costumes and make-up. I was playing an older woman, so we had to draw lines on my face and spray my hair to make it a bit grey. **18**........ Suddenly it was 7.30 and the stage curtains opened. My parents were in the front row!

At first everything went well, and the audience laughed at all the jokes. Then disaster! Ben was supposed to walk up to the window, but he tripped over a chair and fell against the wall. It started to fall forwards, and everyone stood completely still. **19**........ Would the wall crash down on top of us? However, it stopped moving. Everyone breathed again. The whole audience cheered!

The rest of the play went well and at the end everyone stood up and clapped loudly. Someone gave me some flowers and I saw my parents smiling. **20**........ The review on the school website said, 'The actors were brilliant, and they didn't let a minor problem affect them.' I'm still not sure that I'd like to repeat the experience!

A For those few seconds we were all wondering the same thing.

B So, a group of us painted them white and hung some pictures on them.

C It was why I didn't feel very confident about playing that part

D Of course, we couldn't have real glass, but my mum made some curtains.

E That meant that we didn't have long to wait until it all started.

F It was a difficult role and I had lots of words to remember.

G That was probably one of the proudest moments of my life.

H It showed me how I might look when I'm my mum's age – scary!

Part 5

Questions 21–26

For each question, choose the correct answer.

Giving an experience as a present

Choosing a gift for a special occasion should be an enjoyable activity, but, as we all know, it can
21............................. very difficult! How many times have you heard someone say: 'What can I get him?
He's got everything!' Perhaps that's true **22**........................... things like clothes, sweets, posters, soaps
etc. These will be used, finished and perhaps **23**........................... away, or just forgotten. So why not
give the person something to remember? An experience.

Experience gifts don't need to **24**........................... a fortune. You could get a cinema ticket or organise
a picnic. **25**........................... your brain. If your cousin is football mad and a friend's dad knows
someone at a football club, perhaps he could help organise a stadium visit? It's worth a try! Even
the gift of a book will **26**........................... the reader with memories that will last a lot longer than a
box of chocolates!

21 **A** take   **B** go   **C** be   **D** find

22 **A** through   **B** according   **C** except   **D** regarding

23 **A** done   **B** thrown   **C** made   **D** lost

24 **A** pay   **B** spend   **C** charge   **D** cost

25 **A** connect   **B** use   **C** think   **D** employ

26 **A** provide   **B** offer   **C** give   **D** involve

Part 6

Questions 27–32

For each question, write the correct answer.

Write one word for each gap.

New Youth Centre

On Saturday I went to the opening of the new youth centre in Starbridge. The old one
27........................... pulled down a year ago because it was dangerous. This new one is in
28........................... same place, in Church Road, opposite the park. However, it's much bigger and
better **29**........................... the old one. It's a very modern design with a lot of rooms for games,
meetings and sports. There's a huge room for drama and music performances, and facilities such
30........................... a small cafeteria and kitchen, showers and everything else you could wish for!

Before they built the centre, young people in the area were asked **31**........................... they would like
to have there. We all wrote down our suggestions and they've included nearly everything we
wanted! It's wonderful. I **32**........................... definitely be one of the first to sign up for some of the
activities on offer!

WRITING

Part 1

You *must* answer this question. Write your answer in about 100 words.

....

Question 1

Read this email from Jan and the notes you have made.

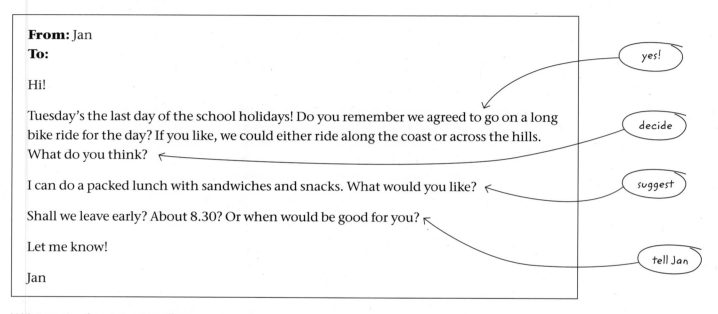

From: Jan
To:

Hi!

Tuesday's the last day of the school holidays! Do you remember we agreed to go on a long bike ride for the day? If you like, we could either ride along the coast or across the hills. What do you think?

yes!

decide

I can do a packed lunch with sandwiches and snacks. What would you like?

suggest

Shall we leave early? About 8.30? Or when would be good for you?

tell Jan

Let me know!

Jan

Write an email to Jan using all your notes.

Part 2

Choose ONE of these questions.

Write your answer in about 100 words.

....

Question 2

You see this announcement on an international website.

> **Articles wanted!**
>
> Have you done something difficult recently that you're very proud of?
>
> Is it important for people to try difficult things?
>
> Write an article saying what you've done and why you're proud of doing it.
>
> The best articles will be published on the website next month.

Write your **article**.

Question 3

Your teacher has asked you to write a story. Your story must begin with this sentence.

When Megan opened the card she got a surprise.

Write your **story**.

LISTENING

Part 1

Questions 1–7

🔊 **10.1 For each question, choose the correct answer.**

---

1 Why is the boy tired?

A   B   C

2 What programme does the girl recommend watching?

A   B   C

3 What did the girl do a lot while she was at the beach?

A   B   C

4 Why is the plane late taking off?

A

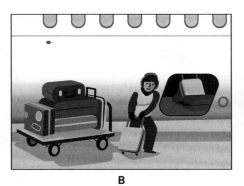

B

C

5 Where will the girl be on July 15th?

A

B

C

6 Which activity will the students do first?

A

B

C

7 Why might the boy be late for the film?

A

B

C

10 Practice test

Part 2

Questions 8–13

🔊 10.2 For each question, choose the correct answer.

....

8 You will hear a boy telling his friend about a car journey.

   What did the boy find surprising about the journey?

   A the music his dad played

   B the time the journey took

   C the route they travelled

9 You will hear a girl telling her friend about an accident with her phone.

   How did she feel after the accident?

   A upset about losing her photos

   B confident she could mend the phone

   C ashamed of getting angry with her brother

10 You will hear two friends talking about learning Spanish.

   In the conversation the boy

   A offers to check the girl's homework.

   B advises the girl to learn vocabulary in a different way.

   C reminds the girl to do her homework on time.

11 You will hear two friends talking about holidays.

   They agree that

   A it's good to visit places in your own country.

   B holidays in your own country are cheaper.

   C the food is better in other countries.

12 You will hear a boy telling a friend about a family birthday party.

   What was difficult about organising the party?

   A deciding which games to play

   B planning everything with no help

   C choosing who to ask to the party

13 You will hear two friends talking about a geography test.

   What does the boy admire about the girl?

   A she plans her revision

   B she writes a lot in tests

   C she is very good at geography

Part 3

🔊 10.3 **For each question, write the correct answer in the gap.**

Write one or two words or a number or a date or a time.

You will hear a teenage writer called David Bennett talking at a book festival about his writing.

A young writer

David started reading at the age of **14**...........................

The early books that David remembers most were about **15**...........................

David's first story was published because of a **16**...........................

David says that he usually writes in his **17**...........................

David uses a **18**........................... to store interesting events.

The action in David's new book happens in **19**...........................

Part 4

Questions 20–25

🔊 10.4 **For each question, choose the correct answer.**

....

You will hear a radio interview with a young singer called Luke who has just performed at a music festival.

20 How does Luke feel after his performance?

    A pleased that it's over

    B excited about his next singing session

    C tired because he was on stage for a long time

21 What does Luke say about his previous experience at this festival?

    A It encouraged him to take up the guitar.

    B It introduced him to lots of local talent.

    C It gave him an interest in performing.

22 Luke has reduced the number of his performances recently because

    A he has done too much travelling.

    B he needs to concentrate on something else.

    C he is preparing for a series of competitions.

23 When did Luke find out he was playing at the Music Weekend?

    A while he was on a bus to town

    B while he was at a family celebration

    C while he was on his way home from school

24 What does Luke say about meeting his heroes?

    A He has appreciated their advice.

    B He has disliked their attitude to non-professional performers.

    C He has felt too shy to talk to them.

25 What will Luke's next step be in his music career?

    A posting music videos online

    B performing his music at events

    C recording his music

SPEAKING

Part 1

Phase 1

🔊 10.5 The examiner will ask you some questions about you. Listen and answer the questions. Pause the recording after each beep and give your answer.

Phase 2

🔊 10.6 The examiner will ask some more questions about you. Listen and answer the questions. Pause the recording after each beep and give your answer.

Part 2

🔊 10.7 The examiner will give you a photograph and ask you to talk on your own about it. Listen and follow the examiner's instructions. Speak for about a minute.

Part 3

🔊 10.8 The examiner will ask you and the other student to discuss something together. Read the task and listen to the examiner's instructions. Discuss the task.

A grandmother's 60ᵗʰ birthday

Part 4

🔊 10.9 Now the examiner will ask you some questions about the topic of the pictures in Part 3. Listen and answer the questions. Pause the recording after each beep and give your answer.

AUDIOSCRIPTS

S.1 and S.2

I'm Kenny. I love holidays in Spain because I can lie on the beach in the sun. I can't swim but I can walk in the water to get cool. Sometimes I stay in the sun for a long time and I get very red! Not a very good idea, I know.

Hi – I'm Seth. We often go to Spain on holiday and it's great. I can speak Spanish so I can talk to people there. My mum and dad can't really, but they know a few words. Sometimes they order strange things in restaurants!

My name's Jimmy. I enjoy our Spanish holidays. I can't sit in the sun because I get bored. I like going to cities, like Barcelona. Then I can see famous places and buildings. A lot of people there can speak English so I can make new friends too.

1.1

A I'm an only child but it isn't a problem for me. I like spending time with my parents, and I've got friends I can see if I want to be with people my own age.

B I come from a big family with nine children, and the house where we live is always very busy, especially in the mornings, when everyone is trying to get ready for school!

C I've got a younger brother and he's really annoying! Like, he always wants to play the same computer game that I want to play, at the only time I'm free to play! There are often arguments in our house! But other days we get on really well.

1.2

1 The biggest swimming pool in the world is at a hotel in Alfonso de Mar in Chile. It's over one kilometre long – that's a lot of water!

2 There are nearly 20,000 bus stops in London. Most of them have a roof to keep you dry, but at the others you may get wet while you're waiting to travel.

3 In the UK, it's against the law to throw waste from your home into a rubbish bin in the street! The ones on the street are only for things you need to throw away while you're out.

4 There were crossings in the streets over 2,000 years ago. In very old Roman cities you can still see places where people could get across the road safely.

5 The tallest apartment block in the world is in New York. It's at 432 Park Avenue, and it has flats on 85 floors.

1.3

1

A: Do you want to meet up on Saturday afternoon?

B: Yeah. Lots of my friends hang out at the shopping centre. We could meet them there.

A: No, I hate shopping! Why don't we go to the skate park? I've got a brilliant new trick I want to show you!

B: Maybe. Or we could go to the cinema? There's a really good comedy film on at the moment.

A: I'd love to see that, but I haven't got any money.

B: OK. I guess it's the skate park, then.

A: Cool.

2

A: Are you looking forward to the summer?

B: Yeah. I'm going to a summer camp. It's by the sea, so you can do water sports.

A: Sounds amazing!

B: Yeah. I've never done scuba diving before, so I'd like to try that.

A: Why don't you try water skiing?

B: No. You have to be very fit and strong for that. I think I'd just fall over!

A: Maybe. I love sailing.

B: Me too. I've tried sailing a few times, and it's fun. But it will be good to do something new.

3

OK, listen everyone. It's nearly time to go home. Before you go, I just want to give you the results of the vote for next month's trip. As you know, there were three ideas. Ice skating didn't get many votes, so that's a no. The most popular choice was the camping trip, so that's what we'll do next month. I'll give you more details next week. Now, the theme park didn't win, but a lot of people chose it, so we'll definitely do a trip there later this year.

4

A: Are you going round to Dan's house on Friday?

B: Yeah. I think about ten people are going, so it should be fun. And his parents are going out!

A: Sounds great. Shall I bring some computer games?

B: No. Dan says no computer games. Emma's got some great music on her phone so she's going to bring that and we're going to listen to music and just relax and hang out.

A: Cool. Will there be anything to eat?

B: Oh, yeah, that reminds me. He wants to have snacks, so perhaps you could get some?

A: Yeah, I'll do that.

5

D = Dad   A = Anna

D: Before you go off to school, Anna, Mum would like to do something as a family next weekend.

A: Yeah, why not? But can it be something fun, like bowling, for example?

D: Well, *you* might call that fun, but your brother doesn't enjoy it, probably because you always win. He'd like to go hiking again.

A: Oh, no. I hate hiking. It always rains!

D: OK. Well, Mum suggested maybe a trip to a museum.

A: Hmm. I know Mum finds museums interesting, but I really don't!

1.4

1 I've got a brilliant new trick I want to show you.

2 You have to be very fit and strong for that.

3 The most popular choice was the camping trip.

4 He wants to have some snacks, so perhaps you could get some.

5 Mum suggested maybe a trip to a museum.

1.5

The photo shows two teenagers, a girl and a boy. They're outside. I can see some water behind them, so I think they're near a lake. There are also some trees on the right. The sky is blue and I think it's summer, but I don't think it is very hot because they are both wearing trousers and trainers. The girl is wearing a shirt and a cap, and the boy is wearing a sweatshirt. They are cooking some food over a fire, maybe for their lunch. They are both smiling, so I think they're having fun.

2.1 and 2.2

I = Interviewer   J = James

I: I'm asking people about their favourite sports. What's yours?

J: Oh – my favourite sport is swimming. I love it! I go swimming every day. I usually train five times a week and swim with friends on the other days. I'm waiting for the bus to go swimming at the moment. My training starts at 5.30. So I'm in a hurry.

I: OK! Who takes you swimming?

J: My mum usually drives me after school during the week and my friend's dad takes us home afterwards. Sometimes at the weekend my swimming club holds races against a different club. Occasionally it's in another town. Then the club gets a coach and the team travels together. It's great fun! And I often win my races!

I: Do you swim every week of the year?

J: Most weeks! But I don't train every week. At the moment we're having a break from training, so today it's just for fun!

AUDIOSCRIPTS

2.3

A: Why are you sitting here? You look really tired. Are you OK?

B: I'm having a break! It's my tennis club's big competition today. We have them every year in June. There are lots of matches. I'm doing very well today. I'm in the final later. It doesn't start until 3.30. So, I'm resting now!

A: I see! I don't play tennis. It's too tiring! Good luck later.

2.4

1

A: Wow! Look at those test results! You're making excellent progress!

B: Thanks! My parents are really pleased.

2

A: Don't waste time chatting online. You've got homework!

B: I know. But I need to talk to Sophie.

3

A: I'm taking part in a tennis competition tomorrow.

B: Good luck! Can I come and watch?

4

A: I spend about two hours practising the piano every evening.

B: That's a long time! I only do half an hour!

5

A: Is your training going well?

B: Yes, thanks. The competition's on Saturday.

6

A: Good! You're doing very well. Keep running!

B: OK, but when can I stop?

7

A: You need to practise the song again and again to get it right.

B: I know – I'm making lots of mistakes.

2.5 and 2.6

OK, well, I go to several clubs but my favourite is the music club. It's on Saturdays but I also practise with a few friends on Friday evenings. Music club is great. In fact, they're looking for more members. There are meetings every week and you can join different groups. I'm 14 so I go to the teen group at 3.30. The children's group meets at 9.30 in the morning and then the adults get together in the evening. All the meetings are at Hill School and we do shows at the theatre in town. It's a lot of fun. We also go on trips to London to see shows. Do you know Mark Manners? He's my dad's favourite singer. He lives in our town. When he isn't busy touring, he sometimes comes to music club to teach us about singing! We have talks sometimes too, by Janet Howard – she's a song writer. Not many people know her but she's very good. That's interesting too. There are also lots of classes at music club. I love singing but I really enjoy finding out about the lights for the stage shows. We're doing a show soon and I'm involved. It's on 15th May and then again later in the month, on the 22nd. Come and see us. And if everything goes dark it's my fault! OK, if you want to join the club I can give you the email address and phone number. Thanks for listening.

2.7

I think going for a walk in the countryside would be a really good idea. What do you think?

What about playing some board games? They're fun for everyone, don't you agree?

Cooking food over a fire is something different. I think everyone would enjoy that.

3.1

At three o'clock last Saturday afternoon, 15-year-old Amy Jones was watching a game of tennis at Wimbledon when something funny happened. One of the players suddenly hit the ball badly, and it flew straight towards Amy. At that moment, Amy was drinking a cup of orange juice. Without thinking, she held up her cup of orange juice and caught the ball in it! Everyone in the crowd thought it was very funny!

And Glen Turner must be the luckiest (or unluckiest man) alive. Six months ago a bear attacked him while he was walking in the mountains in Colorado, USA. Glen fought the bear, which finally ran off, leaving him with just a few cuts. Then yesterday, Glen was swimming in the sea off Florida. He didn't see that a shark – one of the most dangerous animals in the sea – was following him. The shark bit Glen's leg, but he managed to swim safely back to the beach. He's fine now and hoping for a quiet few months!

3.2

1 It's always exciting when you find something strange on a beach. I was walking on a beach a few years ago when I found a huge number of bananas – there were thousands of them. I think they had fallen off a ship!

2 I once found twenty toy ducks on a beach near me. They were just ordinary yellow plastic ducks, but it was really funny to see them there. It seems they came from a ship that sank, and of course because they're very light they just floated on top of the water and ended up on the beach.

3 I keep hoping I'll find something valuable on the beach near me, but in fact I don't think I'll ever find anything to make me rich. I did once find a wooden box that's quite useful for keeping things in.

3.3 and 3.4

H = Host   N = Naomi

H: Hi. Today's show is about storytelling, and I'm with Naomi Green. Naomi teaches storytelling, and she's also written a book about it. What got you interested in storytelling?

N: Well, like all young children I loved listening to stories, at home and at school. But it was when I was touring around Morocco with a friend that I heard this wonderful storyteller – that's when I realised the magic of storytelling. So, when I came back I started doing some myself, at festivals.

H: Why are some people great storytellers?

N: At first, I thought that some people were just naturally good at storytelling. Then I did a course, and I realised that there are lots of things you can learn. But above all, it comes down to spending time going over and over the stories, until you're ready to tell them.

H: How should you choose a good story to tell?

N: You know, above all you have to enjoy the story because you won't tell it well if you don't! Some people get worried about details, like 'Is the ending exciting or original enough?', or 'Will my audience understand it?' But these things are all much less important.

H: I see. So, once you've chosen a story to tell, how should you prepare?

N: Well, of course you have to learn all the details of the story. People often ask 'should I take out the dull parts or make it more modern?' But I think the audience will be interested if you're interested, so you need to really feel the story yourself – almost believe it's about you. Then you'll tell it well.

H: And what about while you're telling the story? What's important then?

N: Well, some storytellers are good at changing their voice for the different characters in the story, and if you can do this, it's great. Above all, you need to connect with your audience: look them in the eye, so they're really listening to you. It's not complicated. You don't need to be an actor, and you certainly don't need to move your arms around madly.

H: And finally, what's the best way to end your story?

N: The big mistake storytellers make is to think they have to explain the meaning of their story. Don't do that! Of course, you don't want to leave your audience feeling confused and guessing how the story ends, but just tell it, and let your audience take their own meaning from it.

H: Thanks for talking to us, Naomi.

3.5

1 I heard this wonderful storyteller!

2 Is the ending exciting or original enough?

3 Should I take out the dull parts, or make it more modern?

4 It's not complicated. You don't need to be an actor, and you certainly don't need to move your arms around madly.

5 You don't want to leave your audience feeling confused and guessing how the story ends.

3.6

I'm going to tell you about something funny that happened to me in an English class. The teacher came in and asked us to take out our books. I was using my phone secretly under my desk, so I reached down and took my book out of my bag without looking. Then the teacher told us which page to turn to. Again, I was busy texting, so I didn't really pay attention. Suddenly, the teacher said, 'Carla, can you read out the first paragraph on page 10?' I quickly opened my book at the right page and started reading. Can you guess what happened next? I continued reading until I realised that the teacher was looking at me angrily, and all my classmates were laughing. I looked down at the book in front of me. It was my history book, not my English book! After what happened, I'm always careful to check which books I'm taking out of my bag!

3.7

Carla was in her English class. She wasn't listening carefully to the teacher because she was texting her friend. Suddenly, the teacher asked her to read something. Carla started reading from her book, but everyone laughed and the teacher looked angry. Then Carla realised her mistake – she was reading from her history book instead of her English book. She was really embarrassed.

4.1 and 4.2

Jack? It's me. I know you're not well at the moment, but I've got the details about the school trip to Bradchester and the Science Museum. That's if you still want to go? The coach leaves school at 8.30 on Friday morning. That's the 5th of June. We arrive at 9.30. We're going round the new robotics exhibition in a group in the morning and then we can walk round the museum on our own for an hour. We're all taking sandwiches and we're going to find somewhere outside by the river to eat them – if it isn't raining! In the afternoon we have a choice of things to do. Amy and Ben are joining the workshop on designing robots. Dave is going to a talk on the history of robotics. I think I'll do that too. Miss Manners is going to give us a mini project to do during the day as well – but she hasn't decided what it is yet! Anyway, the coach gets back to school at 5.15. So, do you want me to put your name on the list? And which afternoon activity would you like to do? Hope you're feeling better! Speak soon!

4.3

1 Don't sit down for a long time when you're working. Stand up and move around after twenty minutes.

2 Make up your mind when to do your homework and then DO it!

3 Tell Katy off if she interrupts you while you're working.

4 Don't hand in your homework late. The teacher doesn't like it.

5 Don't worry if the teacher crosses out things in your homework. Learn from it.

6 Note down exactly what the teacher wants you to do for homework or you'll do the wrong things!

7 If something's difficult get up and walk around for a bit. Then settle down again and it will be easier.

4.4, 4.5 and 4.6

1

A: Danny from swimming club told me he doesn't go to school.

B: What? But he's only 13, like us!

A: His parents teach him at home. He does the same lessons as us, but they can choose their timetable. He doesn't have to get up early if he's tired. I'd love to do that!

B: I guess he learns a lot, but I would get bored without any classmates.

A: Perhaps. But he belongs to lots of clubs, so he meets other people there.

B: OK. I'm sure he gets good grades, but I don't think I'd like it.

2

A: I'm learning Spanish with this new app – it's great! We're going on holiday to Spain this summer and I was worried about not understanding people.

B: OK. How does it work?

A: I do some exercises first on the app, then I record my voice and check my pronunciation. I can join in with an international class online too. The teacher's Spanish and I'm learning really quickly!

B: Does she speak in Spanish all the time?

A: Yes, but it isn't a problem, she speaks very clearly. I only started two weeks ago, but already I can have a short conversation. It's amazing!

3

A: My cousin's at a school in Sweden and he says it's very unusual.

B: Really? Do they have different subjects to us?

A: Well, the subjects are more or less the same, but it's really the design of the school that is unusual.

B: I guess the buildings are quite modern compared to ours.

A: They're very new, yes, but they don't have individual classrooms like ours, with closed doors. He shared some photos online and there's a big room with small groups of relaxed students sitting on bright orange sofas with the teachers sitting on the floor!

4

A: Are you going to the party at our old primary school?

B: What party?

A: The school is 100 years old on Saturday. There's a party for old students and teachers.

B: Sounds fun! I'd love to meet up with some of our friends.

A: I'd like to see our old music teacher. She was really kind to me.

B: I'd also really like to see if the classrooms are the same.

A: Yes, and do you think they still have the pictures of the animals on the wall in classroom 2. I loved looking at that.

5

A: Did your dad go to our school when he was young?

B: No. He went to a small village school. His family lived in the country. There were only eight children in his class!

A: Wow! My dad had 38 in his. They sat in long rows of desks with the teacher at the front. He says the lessons lasted a long time and they weren't allowed to speak.

B: Yes! They just listened to the teacher. He thinks it's great that we have discussions and ask questions all the time.

A: Yeah – my dad says it's a different world!

4.7 and 4.8

E = Examiner S = Student

E: Your photograph shows some friends meeting up. Please tell us what you can see in the photograph.

S: OK. Yes, this photo shows some friends together. There are three people – two girls and a boy. They're sitting on the grass and they're talking. They look relaxed and happy together. We can see two of their faces, but one girl is facing away from the camera. I think they might be in a park. Or maybe they're at school. There is a big beautiful building behind them – I don't know what it is, but it might be their school. Or they might be older and this is their university. Yes, I think that's probably right.

5.1

A: Is this an old photo of you?

B: Yes. My hair was shorter then, so I look quite different.

A: It looks nicer now that it's long.

B: Thanks.

A: Are you going to buy those trainers?

B: Are you joking? They're the most expensive ones in the shop! I'm sure I can find some in another shop that are better value.

A: What's the worst piece of clothing you've ever bought?

B: Some bright pink boots! They're also the least practical thing I've ever bought, because they were really uncomfortable!

A: Why do you always wear jeans?

B: I guess I just feel more comfortable in jeans than in other clothes. You love wearing unusual clothes, but I'm less adventurous than you, and I prefer to wear things that I'm comfortable in. We're all different!

5.2

I guess I'm quite short because I'm only 1m 60 tall. I've got fair hair, although I'd prefer to have really dark hair! I love clothes, but I don't often wear make-up.

I'm average height, not very tall or very short. I'm also quite slim, because I do a lot of sport. I've got long hair which is also curly. It's annoying because it's difficult to style.

Most of my friends are taller than me because I'm quite small for my age, although I hope I'll keep growing.

5.3 and 5.4

Right, everyone, listen please. I'd like to give you some details about our school fashion evening. Today's the 24th of June, and the fashion evening is next Saturday, the 28th. Tickets went on sale on 20th, and we've already sold 200, which is magnificent! Of course, our spectacular fashion show is the main event of the evening, but doors will open at 6 p.m., and between 6 and 7.30 there's a chance to look round the clothes stalls before the show, which is at 8 p.m. There will be ten different clothes stalls, and they've all promised to reduce their prices for the night, so look out for bargains! Unfortunately, we couldn't get a fashion designer or colour expert to come, but we will have a hair stylist who can talk to you about what styles suit you. As you know, all the fashion models in the show will be students, and we still need a few more models, if you want to take part. Mrs Daniels wants to meet all the models on Friday. Please go to the music room at one o'clock. She'll take you down to the hall and show you which rooms you'll use as changing rooms, so you'll know where to come on Saturday. After the show, we're serving refreshments – just drinks and small snacks. These won't be in the reception area, as it says on the posters, but in the gym, which is more convenient because it's closer to the school kitchen. Finally, don't forget the second-hand clothes stalls. You can bring clothes to sell that you no longer want. They must be in good condition, and you can also bring jewellery to sell, but no shoes or make-up please. OK, I think that's everything, so we'll hope to see you all on Saturday!

5.5

1   We've already sold 200 tickets, which is magnificent.
2   The main event is our spectacular fashion show.
3   They've all promised to reduce their prices for the night.
4   After the show, we're serving refreshments.
5   Don't forget the second-hand clothes stalls.

5.6

I can see two people. One is a girl and the other is probably her mother. The girl looks about 12 years old, and she's wearing a light-coloured top. They're in a clothes shop, and they're looking at some jeans. The mother is holding the jeans and the girl is looking at them. I think maybe the girl wants to buy some new jeans and her mother is helping her choose them. The mother looks happy because she's smiling. The girl isn't smiling a lot, but she looks interested in the jeans. I think she might like them, so her mother will probably buy them for her.

6.1, 6.2 and 6.3

So, you're going to the safari park tomorrow? It's brilliant – we went last month. You can drive through the whole park and see some amazing animals! There are a lot of rules about what you can and can't do but a very important one is that you mustn't feed the animals.

Obviously, you can't get out of the car, and I don't think you'd want to, especially going past the lions! There's a monkey area and you must keep your windows closed! They're really naughty and sometimes they climb all over the car. They broke off the car mirrors when we went. But you don't have to drive through if your parents are worried about the car. You can leave the car in the car park and get a bus ride. Also, you don't have to go through the enclosures first. We visited the gardens and the museum in the morning and then drove through the park in the afternoon. The animals were calmer then. And you must take some photos to share on Instagram – especially of the monkeys! Have fun!

6.4

A: These photos of animals are all brilliant, but we have to choose just one for the project. It's hard! I like this one – where the seabirds are diving into the water from high up in the sky to catch the fish. Their wings are so powerful. Or this one, where the bird is landing on a rock to dry its feathers.

B: Yeah – they're both cool. But my favourite is the dolphin which is jumping out of the water, using its powerful tail to lift itself into the air. The penguins are amazing too – in this picture they're hunting for fish – sometimes they swim more than a hundred miles! And this picture where they are climbing up the rocks and steep paths to feed their babies is great. They look so tired but happy.

A: Or what about this picture of the catfish – it's biting a smaller fish that it has caught, and you can see all the sharp teeth!

6.5

Sharks can be very dangerous fish. They can bite and kill humans if they are swimming because they think they are sea animals that they hunt for food. These animals, like other fish, don't have fur or feathers, but they've got very smooth bodies, without the scales that fish normally have, to travel through the water easily. When they are hungry they find big groups of fish and attack them from underneath. Some sharks can survive in both salt and fresh water, and the biggest sharks can grow up to 4.6 metres! They don't usually eat other sharks, but they sometimes fight each other if they are kept in sea life centres.

6.6 and 6.7

1

N: What can the girl see from her bedroom window?

A: Hi! How's the new house?

B: Oh, it's amazing! It's so good to be out of the town. Before, it was really noisy in my room because of all the cars and buses outside. Not like your room with your great view of the park!

A: I know, I like looking at the trees and grass. But now you can too!

B: Yes – there's a river at the end of our garden, and horses too. It's lovely.

A: And better than my view – no people with sandwiches sitting on benches!

2

N: What's the weather going to be like in England at the weekend?

A: If you're on the roads this weekend, then this information is important. Sadly, the weather is going to change. We won't see the sun again until the middle of next week. Winds will affect driving in Scotland, but England will escape them for now. However, there will be a lot of rain in all areas and roads might be dangerous after the dry weather. Lastly, the roads to the coast will be busy this weekend, so please be careful! Listen for our next driving information update, at 7.30 this evening.

3

N: How did the boy get to the beach?

A: Hi Dan! Did you have a good day at the beach?

B: Yeah thanks – it was great, although my legs hurt a bit now.

A: Don't tell me you walked there and back?

B: Hey – walking's good for you! I planned to walk there this morning, but Annie wanted to catch the bus, so we went to the bus stop. My brother was driving to work and stopped to see if we needed a ride, but he was going in the wrong direction. The bus never came – so in the end I got my exercise!

4

N: What did the girl see yesterday?

A: Hi Ben, it's Kelly. I saw something amazing yesterday evening. You know I love foxes and I often watch them cross our garden at night. There's a family of them living in the trees by the river. Once I even saw some baby foxes lying in the sun on the grass at the end of the garden – so cute! But last night we were driving through town and there were two big foxes standing by the side of the road waiting for us to go past – just like people do! Check out my photo on Facebook.

5

N: How did the boy get the information he needed?

A: So, was the photo exhibition good?

B: It was interesting, yes. We had a whole list of quiz questions from the teacher and I think I found most of the answers. There are guides there to explain the pictures, but they were all busy unfortunately. So we bought a leaflet about the exhibition and read about the pictures as we looked at them. I also downloaded a video about the exhibition which was good, but it didn't give any answers to the quiz.

6

N: Which is the girl's newest phone app?

A: I like your phone. Is it new?

B: Yeah – I've got some great apps.

A: I bet they're all about nature and animals!

B: You're right! Look. With this one you can report different insects you see. There's a big survey happening about insect numbers. I used it a lot on my last phone too. This one I got yesterday. It helps recognise different birds by their songs!

A: Wow! What about this one with the tree logo?

B: I've had that one for a long time too – it's great. It tells you about the best walks in different areas.

7

N: What is the girl going to pack?

A: Tom, I wanted to say goodbye. I'm flying to Italy tomorrow to stay with my friend.

B: Lucky you! Is the weather good there at the moment?

A: It's really, really hot, so I don't have to take warm clothes, like coats and things. Just some comfortable flat shoes because we're doing some walking.

B: That's good. Your case won't be too heavy!

A: Well, I've also got some books for my friend's parents, and I'm taking a fun woolly hat for Maria – it gets quite cold in winter there!

B: Great idea – have fun!

6.8 and 6.9

A: OK, shall we start with the map? A map is important when you're walking in the hills, isn't it? It's easy to get lost! What do you think?

B: Yes, you're right. If there aren't many people in the area it can be dangerous. I'm not sure about taking an umbrella.

A: On a walk in the hills? I don't think so! If it rains they've got jackets with hats. No.

B: And if it's very rainy *and* windy it could cause problems!

A: I agree. How about the sandwiches? I think they're really important. The people will walk a long way and they'll get hungry.

B: I disagree because they're quite heavy to carry. I think chocolate bars are better. They're small and easy to put in your pocket.

A: I'm not sure about that. I'd like sandwiches. It's nice to sit down and share a snack after walking for a while. It's not the same to share a chocolate bar! And after you eat the sandwiches you have energy for longer.

B: OK! So, what do you think about the torch? If they get home late it might be dark.

A: Yes, I agree with you. They don't want to fall over and have an accident. But in my opinion the strong boots are the most important thing to have when you go walking in the hills. If they don't wear the right boots they can hurt their feet.

B: You're right. Good boots are important if it's wet or dry.

A: Yes, it's more sensible to have those than a map or a torch. Everyone has a phone these days and there are maps and torches on phones! They don't need them.

B: I agree, the boots are the most important thing. They're definitely more important than sandwiches!

A: OK, they can take chocolate bars!

7.1

1 You can eat pizza all over the world, but one country has a law which says what ingredients restaurants are allowed to put on their pizzas. This country is Italy.

2 The ancient Greeks were people who enjoyed their food! They mixed honey and fruit with snow to make a kind of ice cream.

3 The name given to someone who is rich or has a lot of power is a big cheese. This is because they had enough money to buy a whole cheese, not just a small slice!

4 There is one popular food which dogs can't eat because it makes them ill. This food is chocolate.

5 The people who first made the tomato sauce we now love to eat with burgers didn't sell it as a sauce. They sold it as a medicine because it contained tomatoes and was good for you!

6 There is one popular meal which American astronauts took with them into space when they travelled to the Moon on Apollo 11. This was hotdogs.

7 The country in the world which produces the most coffee is Brazil.

8 Americans who love pasta celebrate National Pasta Month every year in October.

7.2

1 I like making pizzas. I usually cook them in a hot oven, so the bottom of the pizza is lovely and crispy. Then, on top, I put lots of juicy tomatoes, and some cheese, which gives that lovely salty taste.

2 We often go to a Vietnamese restaurant in town that has amazing noodles. They are soft and full of flavour. You can ask them to make them spicy if you like hot food, but I don't. I tried making them at home once but I did something wrong because they were black and burned on the bottom!

3 My mum makes this amazing chocolate dessert. It's like a small cake. There's lots of sugar and chocolate in it, so it's really sweet, then she only puts it in the oven for a short time, so it's cooked and quite hard on the outside but still lovely and soft on the inside – mmm!

4 My friend Hana makes amazing sushi. You have to cook the rice, of course, but all the other ingredients are raw. It's made with fish and rice, and lots of Japanese pepper, so it's quite spicy. It's really good for you, and it's easy to make because it can't go wrong – you don't cook the fish, so it can never be burned!

7.3 and 7.4

1

A: Thank you.

[*sound of a door closing*]

A: [*calling*] Jack. The takeaway's here.

B: Cool. I'm really hungry! And pizza's my favourite. I'm looking forward to this.

A: Right. Let's have a look. [*sounds of opening a box*] Ooh, they're still nice and warm. That's one good thing at least.

B: I agree. Cold pizza's horrible!

A: Right. There you go. There's yours, with tomatoes, onions and pepper. That's what you asked for, isn't it?

B: Yeah, it's the right pizza, but there isn't enough tomato, and the base is all soft – it should be nice and crispy!

A: Oh, dear. Mmm. Mine's OK, though. Do you want a bite?

2

A: Did you see that new cookery show last night?

B: No. I can't stand TV cookery shows! Why do people always cry when their dishes go wrong?

A: Well, I don't mind that, but this show is a bit different. They aren't trying to win anything.

B: So, what's it about?

A: Well, the idea is to get chefs from different countries together so they can share their cooking traditions with each other. Then they work together to create new dishes.

B: Oh, that sounds more interesting.

A: Yeah. You get lots of useful tips you can try yourself too. You'd enjoy it.

3

A: Right, shall we get started?

B: Yes, please. I love making cakes, and your spicy chocolate cake is amazing!

A: Thanks. Well, this is the list of ingredients. You have to make sure you check the weight of the sugar, flour and butter carefully, otherwise you won't get good results. Apart from that, it's a really easy recipe to follow. You cook it slowly so you don't have to worry about getting the oven just right. It does take quite a long time to prepare, but it'll be quicker with two of us.

B: Great. So, what's first?

4

A: Are we all ready for the barbecue on Saturday?

B: I think so. My mum bought us some burgers, and some stuff for salad.

A: What about Lucy? She doesn't eat meat.

B: Don't worry. I've got some veggie burgers too.

A: Great. What about desserts? My mum's got some really nice recipes for desserts. You like cooking, don't you?

B: Yes, but we haven't got time. Let's just buy some.

A: OK. And what about drinks?

B: We probably need some more. I guess people wouldn't mind buying some on their way?

A: OK. Let's ask them.

B: Cool. All we need now is sunshine!

5

G = Girl   C = Coach

G: Mr Evans, can I ask you something about the match tomorrow?

C: Sure.

G: I want to play well, so what should I eat, to give me lots of energy?

C: Well, it's important is to get a good night's sleep before the match. So just have something light in the evening – maybe some pasta – not too much.

G: OK. What about in the morning?

C: You don't want to play with a full stomach, so don't fill yourself up at breakfast. But it's a good idea to have something just before you start – maybe a banana or a chocolate bar.

G: Thanks. I'll do that.

7.5

The photo shows two women. The woman on the left is eating something. It looks like a cookie which they've made. The other woman is going to take one too. In front of them is something white. I'm not sure of the word in English, but it's something you use for making cookies. They're both wearing something over their clothes. I can't remember the word in English, but it's a type of cover for your clothes, to keep them clean when you're cooking.

AUDIOSCRIPTS

7.6

W = Waitress   L = Lena   A = Amina

W: Hello. Are you ready to order?

L: Yes, please. I'd like a burger with chips.

W: And for you?

A: I'll have the same, please.

W: What would you like to drink?

L: I'll have a milkshake, please.

W: Large or small?

L: Just a small one, please.

A: And I'll have a diet cola, please.

W: OK, I'll be right back.

8.1 and 8.2

A: Hi! We arrived at the hotel at lunchtime and it's fantastic!

B: Have you been to the beach yet?

A: Yes, I have. It's lovely – white sand, and I've never seen water so blue!

B: You're so lucky!

A: Have you ever been to Malta?

B: No, never. I've been to some beaches in Spain, Italy and France but not Malta.

A: This is my first visit and I love it!

B: You mustn't waste time. Go and unpack your bags and get onto the beach!

A: I've already unpacked. I did that an hour ago. But I haven't been round the hotel yet. I want to find the indoor pool and gym.

B: Have a great time. And don't forget your sun cream!

A: Yes, I've just put some on! See you!

8.3

1 I was looking forward to the arrival of my friend from Italy but there was a delay and I had to wait two hours.

2 We took four cases to the USA but all our luggage got lost so we had to buy new clothes.

3 You need insurance when you go on holiday because you might be in an accident.

4 We went on a day trip and we had a guide on the coach to tell us about the different places along the route.

5 We missed the bus into the town because there was a mistake on the timetable, so we took a taxi. Luckily we caught the bus back!

6 My dad's travelled a lot by car but he's still bad at following directions.

8.4 and 8.5

I = Interviewer   M = Mason

I: Mason Barnes has just returned from a school skiing trip to Switzerland. Hi Mason! So, why did you decide to go on this skiing trip?

M: Well, I missed last year's school trip to Italy because I wasn't well. This skiing trip was a bit close to my exams but I really wanted to learn how to ski, so my parents agreed!

I: It was your first time skiing?

M: Yes! I was with the beginners. I didn't mind that, but some students in that group were a bit angry because they weren't with their friends, who were in the advanced group. Skiing is very difficult, and it was good to learn from the beginning. I learned quite quickly, which amazed me!

I: I hear you had a problem on the fourth day.

M: Yes – a big problem! Skiing was OK, but it was stopping that was difficult! I was skiing down a hill, very fast. I was thinking – oh I'm getting really good! And then I couldn't stop at the bottom! I hit one of my friends. We fell over and his ski went into my leg. I hurt my knee and the doctor said I had to stop skiing. So I spent the rest of the holiday in the hotel!

I: Oh no! Did you get very bored?

M: Well, in fact, I had a really good time! It meant that I could enjoy being in Switzerland, and not just the snow. I made friends with some young Swiss waiters. Their English wasn't very good, so I practised my French and they told me lots of things about Swiss food and national costumes. I planned to do some studying, but in the end I didn't have time. It was brilliant!

I: Is there anything you'd like to change about your trip?

M: My classmates had fun, but they didn't really do anything apart from ski, take a few photos and chat to each other. So, actually, I think I learned more than they did! I'm sad I only saw one small part of Switzerland while I was there, but there's always another time. It's a lovely country.

I: So, do you think you'll see your Swiss friends again?

M: Definitely. I email one of them, Marcel. He's a year older than me. He's at the hotel for part of the skiing season. Next summer holiday he wants to find a job at a hotel in London before he goes back for his last year at school in Geneva, Switzerland. I'm planning on staying with him and his mum and dad in Geneva next year. He can show me around the city. Much better than skiing!

8.6 and 8.7

T = Tom   M = Molly

T: Hi! How are you enjoying the school trip? Are you speaking a lot of Italian?

M: It's cool! We're learning a lot about the history and culture. We've been here for a week now and I love it! We've seen lots of amazing things since we arrived in Italy! We're in the beautiful city of Venice at the moment and yesterday we were in Rome. But it's really hot. It's been over 30 degrees since 10 o'clock this morning.

T: I've visited Venice and I remember the heat.

M: Katy's not very well. She's had flu for a few days and she hasn't been out of the hotel room since yesterday morning.

T: Oh, poor Katy. One of my friends has been ill with flu too for a week. I hope she's better soon. What a horrible way to spend your school trip. Are you OK?

M: Yes, thanks. I've had a headache for a couple of hours, but I think that's the sun – and the crowds. I haven't seen so many people since I was in London last summer.

T: Well, be careful. And enjoy the rest of the trip!

M: Thanks! On to the city of Florence tomorrow for another day of culture!

8.8 and 8.9

V = Vera   T = Tomas

V: OK, we need to think about a present for the girl's parents. Shall we start with the book of photos? I think that's a nice present. The photos show different parts of the city. They can keep it and look at it in the future. What do you think?

T: Yes, it's a nice idea. But I think these kinds of books can be quite heavy to carry. And they're usually quite expensive.

V: I agree with you. What about the biscuits? I would love to get biscuits! The only problem is that they will eat them and then the present is gone!

T: Yes, you're right. But you can buy biscuits in a pretty box or tin, perhaps with a picture on it. They can use the box in the future.

V: Perhaps. I'm not too sure. Let's think about the coffee cups. In my opinion they're quite nice but you can buy coffee cups anywhere.

T: Yes, I agree. They're not from just one city. She wants to take something that is from THIS city. You know, I really like the t-shirt.

V: Me too! It's a nice memory, and useful too. The parents can keep that forever! I think they would love it. They can show it to all their friends! Oh, but the only thing is she would need to buy one for each of them. That might be expensive.

T: Yes that's true. Well, what about a key ring? I'm not keen on that. You get those in every tourist shop and they usually break.

V: Yes. People keep them for a short time, and then they throw them away. They're a bit boring. And finally, we've got the recipe book of local dishes. I like that idea too. What do you think?

T: I'm not sure about that. I think it's a present for the person who does the cooking. Not for both the mum and dad.

V: Mmm. I don't agree with you. I think it's a present for the whole family. Everyone eats the meals! OK, we've talked about all the presents now. Shall we decide on the best one?

T: OK. I would definitely choose the T-shirt, or maybe the biscuits.

V: And my choice would be the biscuits or the recipe book. We both like the biscuits, so shall we choose them?

T: Yes, I'm happy with that. Let's choose them.

9.1

1

A: What do you usually do at the weekend if you don't have any homework?

B: When I have time, I work as a volunteer at a pet rescue centre. I love animals!

2

A: What are your plans for the weekend?

B: If it's warm, I'll go sailing with my dad – it's great fun!

A: And what will you do if the weather isn't good?

B: I'll probably watch sport on TV!

3

A: I need to go home now. My parents will be annoyed if I'm late.

B: I know what you mean! My mum always gets worried when I don't get home on time.

4

A: When I feel bored, I always watch a movie.

B: That's a good idea. I `ll try that next time I have nothing to do!

5

M = Mum   D = Dad

M: I don't feel like cooking. If you make us dinner tonight, I'll wash the dishes.

D: OK, I'll make something when I finish this game.

9.2

1 I need to call my friend, but I can't switch my phone on. I was using it all morning, and now there's no power left. My battery is dead.

2 I want to get onto this website, but I can't. It keeps asking me for my secret word and I can't remember it. I've forgotten my password.

3 I really want to download this app, but I've already got lots of apps on my phone, and it's full. I've run out of memory.

4 It's really difficult to watch films on my tablet at home. They keep stopping. It's so annoying! We don't have a good connection.

5 It's my birthday soon, so I want to invite some of my friends to come to my house. My parents say it's OK for them to come and watch a film, but not to stay the night. They won't let me have a sleepover.

9.3 and 9.4

Right, listen everyone. I know you're excited, and I'm sure the science fiction convention will be a great experience. I just need to give you a few details. First, the trip is next Saturday. You need to be at school at eight o'clock, so the bus can leave at 8.30. We'll get to the convention at 9.30. We'll be indoors all day, so you don't need coats, and we'll organise drinks, but it's a good idea to have some sandwiches with you because the queues for food are always quite long. There are lots of great events during the day, like a movie make-up display in the morning, and a quiz after lunch, which should be fun. There's also a group photo before lunch, for everyone wearing costumes, which will be great to see.

There are lots of stalls where you can buy things, but most things are very expensive. However, it's worth looking at the books, which are good value, but I suggest you don't waste your money on things like T-shirts or toys that you can get cheaper online. You're free to spend the day as you like. Just make sure you're back in time to get the bus home at the end of the day. There's a meeting point near the café, but that's usually very busy, so we'd like you to come to the main entrance, so we can walk down to the car park together to travel back. Finally, I'm going to post some information about our trip on the school website. When you get back, you can write a review of the convention and upload it to the website, and the best one will win two cinema tickets. You can also upload photos from the day, or a short story – science fiction, of course! Any questions?

9.5

There are five people in the photo, two girls and three boys. They're outside, maybe in a park, I think, and they're having a picnic. They're sitting on the grass. I guess it's probably summer because they aren't wearing coats. It looks sunny too, but it's not too hot because they aren't wearing shorts and T-shirts. I can't remember the word in English but they are sitting in the darker bit that isn't sunny. There are some books on the grass so I think they might be students – so maybe it's their lunch break. Both girls have got long hair and the one in the middle is wearing a dark top and patterned trousers. The boy in the middle has got short black hair. He's wearing a sweatshirt and jeans. He's also wearing … I'm not sure of the word in English, but they go on your arm. The boy on the right is wearing a patterned shirt. They all look very happy and relaxed, so I think they're good friends. There are some trees behind them, and some houses. There's a big … I don't know the word in English, but it's a kind of plant. It's something you grow around your house like a fence.

9.6

1 There are five people in the photo.

2 Most of the friends are eating a sandwich.

3 The friends are sitting on the grass.

4 The two girls in the photo have long hair.

5 There are some buildings and trees behind them.

6 There are some books in front of them.

9.7

1 I can't remember the word in English.

2 I'm not sure of the word in English.

3 They go on your arm.

4 I don't know the word in English.

5 It's a kind of plant.

6 It's something you grow around your house.

9.8

There are three people in the photo, two boys and a girl, I think, but we can't see the third person very well. They're outside, in the countryside. I think they're probably hiking because they're carrying backpacks. There is one girl, and she's got long hair. I don't know the word in English, but she has her hair organised so it isn't in her face. She's wearing a T-shirt and a shirt over the top. The boy we can see well is wearing a T-shirt. The other boy has something around his head. The weather is dry, but it isn't sunny. It's quite cloudy. The people look quite hot but they're hiking so maybe that's why! They look tired, but they look quite happy. The girl is smiling. Maybe they're stopping to let the boy at the back of the photo get something out of his bag.

10.1

N = Narrator

1

N: Why is the boy tired?

A: Hi! You look tired.

B: Yes, I am. I need an early night.

A: I heard about your new baby sister. Is she keeping you awake at night?

B: She was. She cried a lot, but now she's good and she's sleeping well. I did a lot of housework yesterday after school to help Mum and Dad because they've been so busy with the baby. I'm really tired! But, about the new baby – we're having a party to celebrate. Would you like to come?

A: I'd love to. Thanks.

2

N: What programme does the girl recommend watching?

A: Tom? It's Angie. I just wanted to remind you about the programme I mentioned yesterday. I guess you'll want to watch the live TV awards at 8.30 as you know all the actors and the programmes! But in case you get fed up, there's live music from the Dorchester festival at the same time. I was there last summer, and it'll be excellent, I'm sure. It follows the cooking competition which I'll watch too, but I don't think that's really your sort of programme! Speak later!

3

N: What did the girl do a lot while she was at the beach?

A: Tell the class your favourite part of the Italian exchange visit, Lizzie.

B: Easy! Going to the beach nearly every day. The weather was very hot, and it was good to have the light wind by the sea. I usually just sunbathe all day on the beach but in Italy I spent most of my time in the water cooling off. My sea swimming definitely improved. There was a hotel along the beach and the guests did activities on the sand to music all morning. I felt tired just watching!

AUDIOSCRIPTS

4

N: Why is the plane late taking off?

A: This is your pilot. As you can see there's been a slight delay in take-off. My apologies for not explaining before, but I've been waiting for information. There were some difficulties earlier loading the plane because of a computer problem but that was solved, and we were ready for take-off at the right time. However, storms over the Atlantic have slowed planes flying into London Airport, our destination. We have instructions to delay our arrival. I apologise for the wait, and I am sure we'll be in the air shortly.

5

N: Where will the girl be on July 15th?

A: Hi! We're going to the Haydown Arts Festival in July. Do you want to come? It's on the 15th and 16th. We're camping.

B: Oh thanks! That would be cool – but I think something's happening that week. Oh, isn't it Joe's birthday on the 15th?

A: That's the following week. He's having a barbecue in his garden. I'm looking forward to it!

B: You're right. I remember now – it's my brother's wedding anniversary. But they're going to Paris this year, so no celebration here. Great – I'd love to come.

6

N: Which activity will the students do first?

A: OK everyone, we're a bit late arriving here in London because of the traffic but we've still got a full afternoon planned. I know many of you want to walk along the River Thames and that is on the list. But the weather will be better later, so we'll do that after the visit to the Monet art exhibition. Don't forget to take notes for your project! We'll have lunch in the café at the gallery before looking at the pictures. Enjoy your visit!

7

N: Why might the boy be late for the film?

A: Hi!

B: Hi! You're still on the train, I can hear it.

A: I know. I might not be there for the start of the film. For some reason we're waiting outside the station, but the train isn't actually delayed yet. It's annoying, because I left half way through football practice to get the 4.30 train but then I had to help mum take our dog to the vet. So I had to get a later train, the 5.00, which I'm on now. If I'm not there at 5.30, go in without me and I'll find you – sit at the back!

B: OK!

10.2

8

N: You will hear a boy telling his friend about a car journey.

A: Hi there! Did you have a good journey back from your cousin's house on Sunday?

B: It was fine, thanks. I thought it was going to take ages because we heard on the radio that there was an accident on the motorway. But the roads were clear when we got there. As usual my dad put on his favourite rock music, so I listened to my music on my headphones all the way. We were back by 4.30 so I had time to do my homework and watch the football before bed!

9

N: You will hear a girl telling her friend about an accident with her phone.

A: You know I got a new phone yesterday?

B: Yes, a really expensive one, wasn't it?

A: Well, my baby brother knocked it into his bath last night.

B: What? How did that happen?

A: I was showing him a game and he knocked it out of my hand and into the water! I shouted at him, he cried, and then of course I felt bad about shouting. I got it out but it doesn't work. Luckily, I have copies of all my photos and music and I'm sure the insurance will pay for a new one.

B: You're right.

10

N: You will hear two friends talking about learning Spanish.

A: My Spanish marks aren't very good again this month. I spend a lot of time learning grammar rules and I copy new words out of the dictionary. But I always make mistakes in my homework.

B: It isn't always a good idea to copy words from a dictionary. Sometimes they aren't very useful. Maybe just try reading some Spanish books and you'll learn new words like that.

A: OK.

B: And remember to look at your homework again when you've finished. You sometimes notice mistakes you've made.

A: Could you look at it for me? Your Spanish is so good.

B: Maybe!

11

N: You will hear two friends talking about holidays.

A: We might go to Croatia for our next holiday. How about you?

B: We're staying in this country. We've never been to the lakes in the north so we're going there. I like going abroad because it's interesting to meet different people. But it's good to find out more about your own country too.

A: You're right. I think going abroad is fun. I love the different food! But there are some interesting parts of this country I should visit too.

B: Exactly! And there are different types of food there too!

A: True. It's less expensive too. Good idea.

12

N: You will hear a boy telling a friend about a family birthday party.

A: Did Molly's birthday party go well?

B: Yeah – surprisingly! My mum and dad did all the food and I organised the games and the music. It isn't always easy to keep my sister and her five-year-old friends entertained, but they seemed to have a good time.

A: I couldn't do that! I'm not as patient as you are.

B: It's planning really. I had other ideas in case they all said, 'Don't want to do that!' Deciding with Molly who to invite in the first place was a problem. She wanted 50 children! In the end we had 10 and it was just right!

13

A: You will hear two friends talking about a geography test.

B: Wow! That was difficult. I didn't finish all the questions.

A: I did them all but I know I got two wrong. I didn't revise those topics.

B: I read everything in our geography notes at least five times. I have to give myself a revision timetable or I wouldn't do anything! I just wrote too much. I always do! I start and then I can't stop!

A: You're so good. I always leave revising until the night before and then I'm too tired to go through everything.

B: We'll have to wait and see how we did!

10.3

It's really exciting to be here to talk about my writing. I've been writing stories since I was about eight years old. My parents always read to me and I learned to read myself quite early, when I was four. So, I've been in love with books for a long time! Those first books were all about animals, but I soon moved on to adventures. and I have to say those stories still stay in my memory.

I started inventing stories to read to my friend on the school bus. He loved them. Then I sent one in to a competition because my teacher suggested it. I won second prize and my story appeared in a magazine. I was so proud!

People ask about where I usually write. I used to write in the school library but these days I've got a study where I can either be quiet or play music if I want to.

Another question I am often asked is about where my ideas for stories come from. Some writers keep a notebook where they write down interesting things they see or hear about. I started doing that, but my notebook was never with me when I wanted it, so I have notes on my phone – that's usually with me!

My most famous books are the ones about murders with my lady detective, Katy Kosta. They all take place in Manchester, which is where I live now. But my latest book is a bit different. It's about homeless people in London and the problems they have. I know people like the detective stories, but I hope that they find this one interesting too. I really enjoyed writing it. I think authors need to try new things in their books from time to time. Now, are there any questions …. [fade]

10.4

I = Interviewer   L = Luke

I: Hi Luke! You've just come off stage after performing at the Open Park Music Weekend. What was it like?

L: Before going on, I was very excited and a bit scared at the same time! But there were a lot of happy faces and people sang along, so I think they enjoyed it. I certainly did. My session went over my time limit and I used up a lot of energy. I need a cold drink and a long sleep!

I: This is your first time singing here, isn't it?

L: Yes, but I've been coming here to listen to the music since I was ten and started playing the guitar. It's great to have a local event like this. I wanted to be up there singing and playing for people. And here I am!

I: You're still at school, so where do you usually perform?

L: It varies. I sing and play my guitar at school events and friends' parties. I've also done a few competitions, which has involved a bit of travelling. I'm studying to go to university next year so I'm not doing much evening singing at the moment. I'm revising a lot, I'm afraid!

I: Were you surprised when you were asked to sing here at the Music Weekend?

L: Yes, very surprised! Most of the musicians here are professional but every year they invite one local singer. I was waiting for the bus home after school when I got the phone call. The organisers said they'd seen me perform at my cousin's wedding party last March. I just sat there for ten minutes, missing two buses!

I: What have you enjoyed most about this weekend?

L: Well, I was a bit shy about meeting some of my music heroes. I thought they might be too busy or think they were too important to talk to someone like me. But they were kind and told me some useful things about singing as a career.

I: So, what are your plans for the future, Luke?

L: I've always wanted to make a music video, and one day I hope to go professional and make lots of albums. But immediately after my exams I want to get back to playing live music at shows again – with luck, while I'm at university. I think that's the best way to try to have a singing career!

I: Well, good luck with everything, Luke. And thanks for talking to me.

10.5

What's your name?

How old are you?

Where do you live?

Thank you

10.6

Tell me what you did yesterday.

How often do you do sports?

Which do you like best, the weekends or weekdays? Why?

Thank you

10.7

Now I'd like you to talk on your own about something. I'm going to give you a photograph and I'd like you to talk about it. Here is your photograph. It shows young people in a race. Please tell us what you can see in the photograph.

10.8

Now, in this part of the test you're going to talk about something together for about two minutes. I'm going to describe a situation to you.

A grandmother is going to celebrate her 60th birthday. Her family want to do something special with her on her birthday. Here are some of the activities they could do with her. Talk together about the different activities and say which you think would be best for the whole family.

10.9

Do you remember the dates of people's birthdays easily?

What was your favourite birthday celebration when you were younger? Why?

Do you like sending cards on people's birthdays? Why / Why not?

Would you like to have a surprise party?

Is it necessary to spend a lot of money on a good present? Why / Why not?

Thank you. That is the end of the test.

The **Cambridge English Qualification B1 Preliminary for Schools Exam**, otherwise known as **Cambridge Preliminary for Schools**, is set at B1 level of the Common European Framework of Reference for Languages (CEFR). It has four separate papers: Reading, Writing, Listening and Speaking. Each paper carries 25% of the marks.

Reading: 45 minutes
Writing: 45 minutes

Listening: 35 minutes (approximately)
Speaking: 12 minutes for

All the examination questions are task-based. Rubrics (instructions) are important and should be read carefully They set the context and give important information about the tasks. All the tasks in the exam, and all the texts you read and listen to, have been specially chosen to reflect the interests and experience of school-age learners of English.

Paper	Formats	Task focus
Reading 6 tasks 32 questions	**Part 1:** multiple-choice Reading five separate short texts and answering one multiple- choice question about each text.	Reading to understand the main message.
	Part 2: multiple-matching Reading descriptions of five people and matching each to one of eight short texts.	Reading to understand specific information and the detailed meaning of descriptions.
	Part 3: multiple-choice Answer five multiple-choice questions about a text from four options.	Understanding of the detailed meaning of the text and attitude/opinions of the writer.
	Part 4: gapped text Choosing sentences to fit into the gaps of a text, with a total of six sentences to place correctly.	Reading to understand how texts are organised and sentences relate to each other.
	Part 5: multiple-choice cloze Choosing the missing word for six gaps from a choice of four listed after the text.	Reading to understand particular words and phrases and use of words for creating meaning.
	Part 6: open cloze Choosing which word is needed to fill each gap in a short text. Six gaps in total.	Reading to understand sentence construction and how words/ phrases relate to each other.
Writing 2 tasks	**Part 1:** email Writing an email of 100 words in reply to a text, covering the points in that text.	Focus on writing an email in an appropriate style and responding to the input text.
	Part 2: longer piece of continuous writing Producing one story or article of 100 words.	Writing using a range of language, creating a well organised text in a particular style.
Listening 4 tasks 25 questions	**Part 1:** visual multiple-choice Seven short recordings, each with a multiple-choice question.	Understanding specific information and detailed meaning.
	Part 2: multiple-choice Six short recordings with one multiple- choice question for each.	Understanding gist, ideas and opinions and agreement/ disagreement.
	Part 3: sentence or note-completion Completing six gaps in a set of sentences/ notes, with words, numbers, or names.	Listening and recording specific information.
	Part 4: multiple-choice Answering six multiple-choice questions about an interview	Understanding detailed meaning of the interview, including the attitudes and opinions.
Speaking 4 tasks	**Part 1:** introduction (2–3 minutes) Answering questions from the examiner about yourself.	Giving personal information, social conversation.
	Part 2: describing a photograph (1 minute each) Individual description of a given photograph.	Using appropriate vocabulary,, organising language to describe what you see.
	Part 3: collaborative Task (2–3 minutes) Two-way conversation between candidates about a task with visual prompts	Maintaining a conversation, responding to others, giving suggestions, discussing alternatives, giving reasons. reasons for your opinions.
	Part 4: discussion (3–4 minutes) Discussion of questions asked by the examiner.	Giving opinions on a range of issues, explaining reasons.

Pearson Education Limited
KAO TWO,
KAO Park
Hockham Way,
Harlow, Essex,
CM17 9SR
England
and Associated Companies throughout the world.

pearsonELT.com/goldexperience

First published 2019
Second impression 2019

ISBN: 978-1-292-19451-6

Set in Camphor Pro

Printed by Neografia, in Slovakia

Acknowledgements
Written by Sheila Dignen and Lynda Edwards.

The Publisher and author would like to thank Liz Gallivan for her feedback and comments during the development of the material.

Picture Credits
The publisher would like to thank the following for their kind permission to reproduce their photographs:

123RF.com: archman 57, bigemrg 53, Anna Bizoń 63, Blue Gum Pictures 83, Pedro Antonio Salaverría Calahorra 12, evegenesis 50, Iakov Filimonov 45, loganban 62, Laurentiu Iordache 11, Jovan Mandic 45, utima 61, Wavebreak Media Ltd 58, zurijeta 40; Alamy Stock Photo: Richard Cooke 23, Directphoto Collection 32, Glow Asia RF 30, H. Mark Weidman Photography 99, Hero Images Inc 70, 79, Image Source Plus 86, Mark Kelly 48, Jack Lowe 25, MBI 72, Ville Palonen 26, Myrleen Pearson 66, Michael Turner 38; Getty Images: Alina555 / E+ 15, Corbis / VCG 76, Steve Debenport / E+ 37, franckreporter / E+ 78, gremlin / E+ 78, Kolbz / iStock 15, M_a_y_a / E+ 63, Onne van der Wal / Corbis Documentary 22, Westend61 74; Heligan Gardens Ltd: "The Lost Gardens of Heligan" by Julian Stephens © Heligan Gardens Ltd 48; Charles Jencks: Black Hole Terrace, GCS Scotland 1996 by Charles Jencks/ With kind permission of The Garden of Cosmic Speculation, Private Garden, Dumfries 48; Pearson Education Ltd: Gareth Boden 32, Jörg Carstensen 86, Handan Erek 30, Jules Selmes 6; Shutterstock.com: Africa Studio 41, 60, AJR_photo 58, Efimova Anna 6, Matushchak Anton 16, Andi Berger 46, Stephane Bidouze 51, Seyms Brugger 51, cheapbooks 58, Cholpan 31, Donna Ellen Coleman 40, Lukashev Dmitry 31, Doremi 20, Dirk Ercken 51, f11photo 30, Sergey Fedoskin 15, fieldwork 51, Fisher Photostudio 59, Fotomicar 86, Gelpi 40, Matt Gibson 54, Christine Glade 86, Anton Gvozdikov 80, Brent Hofacker 82, Helen Hotson 52, Incomible 18, Tory Kallman 51, Aman Ahmed Khan 66, I kouptsova 66, Rina Kozorog 32, Holly Kuchera 51, 57, Hugh Lansdown 51, LightField Studios 35, 58, Nina Lishchuk 68, Mmini 44, Lina Mo 57, Monkey Business Images 8, 11, Nadezda Murmakova 57, Norb_KM 40, Somyot Pattana 28, Pi-Lens 7, polya_olya 66, Pressmaster 5, 24, ProStockStudio 34, Rawpixel.com 33, 43, Romariolen 59, sanupot 32, Menno Schaefer 51, silverkblackstock 86, StevenRussellSmithPhotos 51, Studio_G 56, TTstudio 5, VH-studio 17, Yakobchuk Viacheslav 37, wavebreakmedia 5, WAYHOME studio 66, zetwe 29

Cover Image: Getty Images: Artur Debat

Illustrated by:

Daniel Limon (Beehive Illustration) pp. 10, 52, 94, 95; Dusan Pavlic (Beehive Illustration) pp. 4, 27; Matt Ward (in the style of Simon Rumble) (Beehive Illustration) pp. 19, 53, 71, 100.

All other images © Pearson Education